Somehow we landed in **Six Notrump**

6
NT

David **Bird**   MASTER POINT PRESS • TORONTO, CANADA

Text © 2009 David Bird

Master Point Press
331 Douglas Ave.
Toronto, Ontario, Canada
M5M 1H2   (416)781-0351
Email: info@masterpointpress.com

Websites: www.masterpointpress.com
                www.masteringbridge.com
                www.bridgeblogging.com
                www.ebooksbridge.com

Library and Archives Canada Cataloguing in Publication

Bird, David, 1946-

    Somehow we landed in six notrump / David Bird.

ISBN 978-1-897106-43-3

    1. Contract bridge–Anecdotes. 2. Contract bridge–Humor.
3. Contract bridge–Fiction. 4. English wit and humor. I. Title.

GV1282.3.B5928 2009   795.41'5   C2008-907544-7

Editor   Ray Lee
Copy editor/interior format   Sally Sparrow
Cover and interior design   Olena S. Sullivan/New Mediatrix

1 2 3 4 5 6 7   13 12 11 10 09

Somehow we landed in **Six Notrump**

For our 2-year-old grandson, Daniel, who has already given us so much pleasure

INTRODUCTION

I have always regarded 6NT as the most enjoyable contract to play. As with any slam contract, a couple of the suits may be solid and this allows you to focus your mind on the remaining suits and the best way to play them. A wealth of cardplay techniques are at your disposal, including avoidance plays, safety plays, throw-ins, unblocking plays, deceptive plays and all sorts of squeezes.

Believe it or not, you hold in your hand a book that contains nothing but 6NT contracts! I have divided it into two halves — fact and fiction. The first half of the book features the world's finest players at work, tackling all manner of 6NT contracts — some commendable, some truly awful. You will have a chance to plan your play in these contracts yourself, before seeing what fate befell the original declarer. The second half of the book contains humorous short stories, featuring many of the characters that I have written about over the past 30 years. You will find the bridge-crazy monks of St. Titus Monastery, including the self-centered Abbot; the nuns of St. Hilda's Convent are there, as are the Rabbi and his entourage. There is further action from the masters and boys of Cholmeley School, and from the missionaries, Brother Tobias and Brother Luke, whose main task in life is to convert the Bozwambi tribe to the Acol bidding system. Finally, there are some tales involving Robin Hood, the Sheriff of Nottingham and the much-maligned Sir Guy of Gisburne. Throughout this entertainment only one contract will be found – you guessed it, 6NT. Although some of these stories have been published in bridge magazines around the world, none of them has appeared in any of my books.

Do you sometimes feel cheated when you pay good money for a book and then find several pages that are mostly white space? It will not happen here. Whenever half a page of white space would have occurred, I have filled it with a play problem set in 6NT. The recommended answer to each quiz will be overleaf, or as near as is possible without it appearing on the facing page. There are 32 such 6NT problems, some relatively easy and some that will cause you to sit back in your chair for a while.

By the time you have finished this book, you will surely consider yourself a world expert on 6NT contracts and look forward to playing there as much as I do. You may even be tempted to steer the auction towards 6NT when you should be in a suit slam or playing safely in a game contract. You can tell your partner that it's all my fault!

Enjoy the book.

David Bird

CONTENTS

PART ONE
6NT - Fact

1. RON ANDERSEN'S 6NT

The USA's Ron Andersen sat South on this deal from the final round of the 1990 World Open Pairs semi-finals in Geneva. Barry Goren (USA) was North.

```
                    ♠ A K J 10 8
                    ♡ Q 5
                    ◇ A 7 3
                    ♣ Q 4 3
     ♠ Q 9 6 4                        ♠ 3 2
     ♡ 3 2          Neither Vul.      ♡ J 10 9 8 4
     ◇ J 10 2       Dealer E          ◇ Q 9 5 4
     ♣ J 9 6 5                        ♣ K 10
                    ♠ 7 5
                    ♡ A K 7 6
                    ◇ K 8 6
                    ♣ A 8 7 2
```

West	North	East	South
Mayer	Goren	Wright	Andersen
		pass	1NT
pass	6NT	all pass	

South's 1NT showed 15-17 points. That was 14 points for the two aces and two kings, plus another 1 point because they needed some tops to qualify for the final. When Malcolm Mayer led the ◇J, Andersen won with the ◇K and took a successful finesse of the ♠10. He continued with the ♡Q and ♡A and then led a low club, the five appearing from West. How would you have viewed the situation after this start?

Andersen reasoned that Mayer, sitting West, could count him for five spade tricks and at least six top winners in the other three suits (three or more hearts, two or more diamonds and one club). That was a total of at least eleven and possibly twelve top tricks. Would a world-class pairs player dream of ducking the ♣K if he held it, possibly handing declarer an overtrick on a plate?

Andersen thought not and backed his judgment by playing low from the dummy instead of calling for the queen. East won with the ♣10 and returned a diamond. When a club to the ace dropped East's king, Andersen had only to repeat the spade finesse and twelve tricks were his. A near-top pairs score resulted.

Andersen's inference on the lie of the club suit could not have been drawn in a team-of-four environment, where an overtrick means relatively little.

2. ELY CULBERTSON'S 6NT

Do 6NT contracts mature pleasantly with age? You can judge for yourself as you absorb this deal described by Culbertson in 1935. (In those heady times, bridge books sold in quantities that are unimaginable nowadays. Culbertson's *Blue Book* on bidding was the first and only bridge book to head the USA's non-fiction bestseller list.)

```
                    ♠ K 7 4
                    ♡ A Q J 10 8
                    ◇ A J 6
                    ♣ K 3
   ♠ J 10 9 8 5 2              ♠ 6
   ♡ 4 3         Neither Vul.  ♡ K 6 5 2
   ◇ 9 7         Dealer S      ◇ Q 10 5 3
   ♣ Q 5 4                     ♣ 10 9 8 6
                    ♠ A Q 3
                    ♡ 9 7
                    ◇ K 8 4 2
                    ♣ A J 7 2
```

West	North	East	South
			1♣
pass	1♡	pass	1NT
pass	4NT	pass	6NT
all pass			

No bidding was given when the deal was published, so I have added a plausible modern auction. West leads the ♠J against 6NT. You win with the ace and run the ♡9, losing to East's king. How will you continue when East returns the ♣10?

East is unlikely to be switching from the ♣Q. If he holds ♣1098xx, West's ♣Q will fall doubleton and you can therefore make a case for withholding the ♣J on the first round of the suit. In the play as Culbertson described it, declarer did cover with the ♣J, drawing the ♣Q and ♣K. How would you have continued from this point?

Declarer cashed the two remaining spade winners, followed by three more rounds of hearts. This was the end position that he reached:

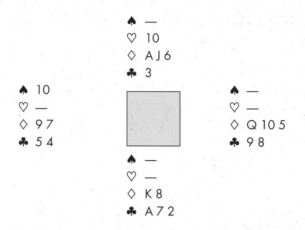

```
              ♠ —
              ♡ 10
              ◇ A J 6
              ♣ 3
♠ 10                        ♠ —
♡ —                         ♡ —
◇ 9 7                       ◇ Q 10 5
♣ 5 4                       ♣ 9 8
              ♠ —
              ♡ —
              ◇ K 8
              ♣ A 7 2
```

When the ♡10 was led from dummy, East had to throw a diamond to retain his club guard. Declarer played a club to his ace, seeing the nine from East, and had no difficulty in reading the lie of the cards. He played the ◇K and ◇A, dropping East's queen, and claimed his slam.

What did you make of that? It was a smart move for declarer to cover the ♣10 with the ♣J, thereby transferring the club guard from the West to the East hand. He also did well to read which cards the defenders held in the end position, since East might have held one club more and one diamond fewer. The instructive point of the deal is that East's switch to the ♣10 was foolish. What could it achieve? He should have returned a passive heart, leaving declarer to do his own work. The slam could then have been made only by the double-dummy line of leading the ♣J from the South hand and running it!

Quiz 1 *How would you play 6NT?*

```
              ♠ A K Q 10 6 5
              ♡ K 8 5
              ◇ 9 3
              ♣ K Q
♡J led        ┌──────────┐
              └──────────┘
              ♠ J 9 2
              ♡ A 7 6 3
              ◇ K 5
              ♣ A 8 6 5
```

West	North	East	South
3◇	4♠	pass	4NT
pass	5♠	pass	6NT
all pass			

How will you play 6NT when West leads the ♡J? **(The answer is overleaf.)**

```
                    ♠ A K Q 10 6 5
                    ♡ K 8 5
                    ◇ 9 3
                    ♣ K Q
   ♠ 8                              ♠ 7 4 3
   ♡ J 10                           ♡ Q 9 4 2
   ◇ A Q J 10 7 4 2                 ◇ 8 6
   ♣ 9 4 2                          ♣ J 10 7 3
                    ♠ J 9 2
                    ♡ A 7 6 3
                    ◇ K 5
                    ♣ A 8 6 5
```

West	North	East	South
3◇	4♠	pass	4NT
pass	5♠	pass	6NT
all pass			

West leads the ♡J and you see that there are eleven tricks on top. With the ◇A marked offside by the bidding, you must seek a twelfth trick in hearts or clubs. The only realistic chance is a squeeze without the count on East. You win the heart lead in dummy to preserve the entry to the hand opposite the squeeze card, dummy's last spade. You then run dummy's winners, arriving at this end position:

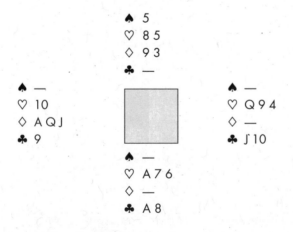

```
            ♠ 5
            ♡ 8 5
            ◇ 9 3
            ♣ —
   ♠ —                    ♠ —
   ♡ 10                   ♡ Q 9 4
   ◇ A Q J                ◇ —
   ♣ 9                    ♣ J 10
            ♠ —
            ♡ A 7 6
            ◇ —
            ♣ A 8
```

East has already had to throw both his diamonds. Even though you have not rectified the count (in other words, you have not deliberately lost a trick to tighten the end position), the last spade squeezes East. If he discards a club, you will score two more club tricks. When he throws a heart, you discard the ♣8 from your hand. You then play the ace and another heart, establishing an extra heart trick.

3. OSVALDO VERGARA'S 6NT

Chile faced Venezuela in the 1984 World Team Olympiad, played in Seattle. On this deal Osvaldo Vergara, South for Chile, arrived in 6NT missing two aces:

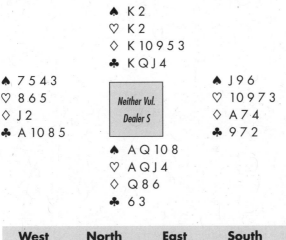

```
                 ♠ K 2
                 ♡ K 2
                 ◇ K 10 9 5 3
                 ♣ K Q J 4
  ♠ 7 5 4 3                         ♠ J 9 6
  ♡ 8 6 5        Neither Vul.       ♡ 10 9 7 3
  ◇ J 2          Dealer S           ◇ A 7 4
  ♣ A 10 8 5                        ♣ 9 7 2
                 ♠ A Q 10 8
                 ♡ A Q J 4
                 ◇ Q 8 6
                 ♣ 6 3
```

West	North	East	South
Vernon	del Villar	Benaim	Vergara
			1NT
pass	2♠	pass	2NT
pass	6NT	all pass	

South's 1NT showed 15-17 HCP and the 2♠ response was minor-suit Stayman. When the 2NT rebid denied four cards in either minor, North decided that only a full-blooded leap to 6NT would do justice to his values.

The Venezuelan West led a spade, Vergara winning with dummy's ♠K. A diamond to the queen won the second trick and he continued with a diamond to West's jack and dummy's king. Roberto Benaim, sitting East, could visualize a critical guess when he took his ◇A. Should he return a heart or a club? Since there was no obvious solution to this dilemma, he decided to wait one more round before taking his diamond trick. This would allow his partner to signal which ace he held, if any.

A third round of diamonds never came! Vergara decided that he had drawn sufficiently from that particular well and switched his attention to clubs. The ♣A lay in the safe hand and he soon had twelve tricks before him.

What was the key to a winning defense? Once declarer had played a diamond to the queen, it was clear that West's ◇J2 could have no trick-taking role to play. His play of the two before the jack should therefore have been taken as suit preference for a club switch. Holding the ♡A instead, he would play the jack and then the two.

4. JEAN-MICHEL BOULENGER'S 6NT

France faced North America in the semi-finals of the 1975 Bermuda Bowl, contested in Bermuda. This was Board 42:

```
                    ♠ Q J 9 7 6 4
                    ♡ 8 7 6
                    ◇ 7 2
                    ♣ 4 3
  ♠ 5 2                              ♠ 8 3
  ♡ A Q 9 5 3 2    ┌──────────┐     ♡ 10 4
  ◇ 9              │ Both Vul. │     ◇ J 8 6 4 3
  ♣ Q 8 7 5        │ Dealer S  │     ♣ J 9 6 2
                   └──────────┘
                    ♠ A K 10
                    ♡ K J
                    ◇ A K Q 10 5
                    ♣ A K 10
```

West	North	East	South
Kantar	Svarc	Eisenberg	Boulenger
			2♣
2♡	pass	pass	2NT
pass	3♠	pass	4◇
pass	4♠	pass	5♡
dbl	5♠	pass	6NT
all pass			

At the other table Swanson and Soloway had arrived in 6♠, played by North, which was speedily dispatched by a heart lead. France would therefore pick up a big swing if Jean-Michel Boulenger could make 6NT. Before we look at the play, what would you have led from the West hand?

It was obvious that a heart lead would give declarer a trick with the ♡K, and Eddie Kantar decided to lead the ♣5. The defenders did not suffer directly from this aggressive lead, since East produced the ♣J, which South won with the ♣A. However, it did leave Kantar in sole control of the club suit.

Boulenger cashed the ♠A and ♠K, everyone following. Before running the remaining spades, he played his three top diamonds, discovering the lie of that suit. He returned to spades and soon arrived at this end position:

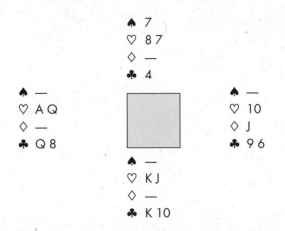

Boulenger led dummy's last spade, throwing the ♡J, and turned to await West's card. Kantar could foresee a throw-in if he discarded the ♡Q. He therefore threw the ♣8, hoping to put declarer to some sort of guess. Boulenger was up to the challenge. He played a club to the king, dropping West's queen, and claimed his slam for a swing of 17 IMPs.

Quiz 2 *How would you play 6NT?*

```
              ♠ A K Q 10 8
              ♡ A K Q J 10
              ◇ 4
              ♣ K Q
♡5 led        [          ]
              ♠ 9 3
              ♡ 8 7 4
              ◇ K J
              ♣ A J 7 6 4 3
```

West	North	East	South
	2♣	pass	3♣
5◇	6◇	pass	6NT
all pass			

North's 6◇ asks you to choose a major suit. With no great liking for either major, and a keen desire to have your efforts appear in this book, you bid 6NT. You win the ♡5 lead in dummy and play the ♣K, West discarding a diamond. What now? **(The answer is overleaf.)**

                    ♠ A K Q 10 8
                    ♡ A K Q J 10
                    ◇ 4
                    ♣ K Q

♠ 6 2   ♠ J 7 5 4
♡ 9 5 3   ♡ 6 2
◇ A Q 10 9 7 5 3 2   ◇ 8 6
♣ —   ♣ 10 9 8 5 2

                    ♠ 9 3
                    ♡ 8 7 4
                    ◇ K J
                    ♣ A J 7 6 4 3

West	North	East	South
	2♣	pass	3♣
5◇	6◇	pass	6NT
all pass			

You win the ♡5 lead and play the ♣K, West discarding a diamond. You can score three clubs by overtaking the ♣Q on the second round, but this would give you only eleven tricks. When you play dummy's top spades, West disappoints you by showing out on the third round. Is there any chance left?

Indeed there is! East has to retain three clubs, otherwise you will overtake the ♣Q and score an extra club trick (or two) in the South hand. He will therefore be in trouble when you cash dummy's remaining hearts. This will be the position:

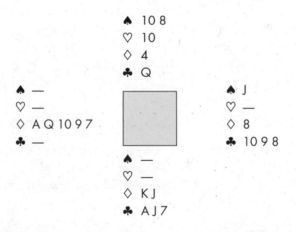

                    ♠ 10 8
                    ♡ 10
                    ◇ 4
                    ♣ Q

♠ —   ♠ J
♡ —   ♡ —
◇ A Q 10 9 7   ◇ 8
♣ —   ♣ 10 9 8

                    ♠ —
                    ♡ —
                    ◇ K J
                    ♣ A J 7

When dummy's last heart is led, East has to release the ◇8, the link to his partner's hand. You cash the ♣Q and put East on lead with a spade. He has to play a club and your ♣A-J score the last two tricks — a stepping-stone squeeze.

5. TIM BOURKE'S 6NT

Australia's Tim Bourke, one of the world's top composers of bridge deals, played this 6NT contract during the qualifying rounds of the 2004 National Open Teams in Canberra:

```
                    ♠ J
                    ♡ A 9 8 5
                    ◇ 4
                    ♣ A K Q J 10 8 2
    ♠ K 9 4 3                          ♠ Q 6 5
    ♡ 7 3           ┌──────────┐       ♡ Q J 10 2
    ◇ 10 9 8 3 2    │ EW Vul.  │       ◇ A J 7 5
    ♣ 9 7           │ Dealer N │       ♣ 5 3
                    └──────────┘
                    ♠ A 10 8 7 2
                    ♡ K 6 4
                    ◇ K Q 6
                    ♣ 6 4
```

West	North	East	South
	Smith		Bourke
	1♣	pass	1♠
pass	2♡	pass	3◇
pass	4♣	pass	4NT
pass	5♣	pass	5◇
pass	6♣	pass	6NT
all pass			

Bourke's 4NT was Roman Keycard Blackwood, with clubs agreed, and the response indicated three keycards. His 5◇ continuation asked for the trump queen, the 6♣ response showing that card but denying any side-suit king.

West led the ◇10 against 6NT. If East had risen with the ◇A, declarer would have had twelve top tricks and you would not have found the deal in this book. A mean-minded East refused to play the ◇A, however, following with the ◇7. How would you have continued after this start?

Bourke spotted a way home if East held four or more hearts, giving him the sole guard of the suit. He ran seven rounds of clubs, forcing East to find five discards. East could see that his red-suit holdings would be more valuable than the ♠Q65, which sat under declarer's spade holding. He therefore released all three spades, a heart and a diamond. These cards were still to be played:

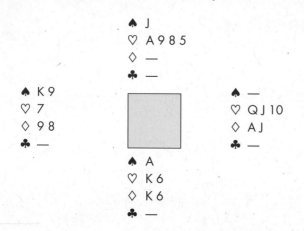

```
                    ♠ J
                    ♡ A 9 8 5
                    ◇ —
                    ♣ —
    ♠ K 9                          ♠ —
    ♡ 7                            ♡ Q J 10
    ◇ 9 8                          ◇ A J
    ♣ —                            ♣ —
                    ♠ A
                    ♡ K 6
                    ◇ K 6
                    ♣ —
```

'Spade, please,' said Bourke, and East had to find one more discard. With no good card to play, he decided to release the ◇J.

There was no guess for declarer, because he needed East to have started with four hearts for a squeeze to work. In any case, the diamond position was fairly clear after the opening lead. Bourke duly led the ◇6 from his hand, bringing down East's bare ◇A, and the ◇K became his twelfth trick.

The play of this deal was an example of a squeeze without the count. In other words, East was squeezed (out of his ◇J) even though the count had not been rectified. Declarer conceded a trick, thereby setting up his own twelfth trick, after the squeeze had taken place.

Quiz 3 *How would you play 6NT?*

```
                    ♠ K 8 4 2
                    ♡ K J 6
                    ◇ A 5
                    ♣ J 10 8 7
    ♠Q led          ▭▭▭▭▭▭
                    ♠ A 6
                    ♡ A Q 4
                    ◇ K J 10 7
                    ♣ A Q 9 2
```

West	North	East	South
2♠	pass	pass	3NT
pass	6NT	all pass	

You win the ♠Q lead with the ♠A, cross to the ♡J and run the ♣J, losing to the king. How will you continue when West persists with another spade honor? **(The answer is on page 25.)**

6. ERIC RODWELL'S 6NT

USA II faced Norway on this deal from the 1997 Bermuda Bowl in Tunisia's Hammamet:

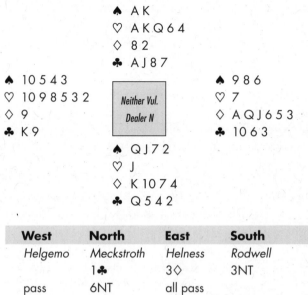

```
                    ♠ A K
                    ♡ A K Q 6 4
                    ◇ 8 2
                    ♣ A J 8 7
♠ 10 5 4 3                          ♠ 9 8 6
♡ 10 9 8 5 3 2    Neither Vul.      ♡ 7
◇ 9               Dealer N          ◇ A Q J 6 5 3
♣ K 9                               ♣ 10 6 3
                    ♠ Q J 7 2
                    ♡ J
                    ◇ K 10 7 4
                    ♣ Q 5 4 2
```

West	North	East	South
Helgemo	Meckstroth	Helness	Rodwell
	1♣	3◇	3NT
pass	6NT	all pass	

Rodwell ended in 6NT after a strong 1♣ opening. The ◇9 was led and Tor Helness took his time before winning with the ◇A and returning the ◇Q. Suppose you had been the declarer. How would you have played 6NT?

Rodwell won the second diamond, as West discarded a small heart, and played a club, successfully finessing the jack. He cashed dummy's two top spades and returned to the bare ♡J to play the other two spade winners. This was the critical position:

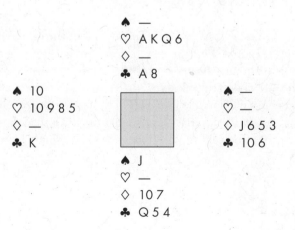

```
                    ♠ —
                    ♡ A K Q 6
                    ◇ —
                    ♣ A 8
♠ 10                                ♠ —
♡ 10 9 8 5                          ♡ —
◇ —                                 ◇ J 6 5 3
♣ K                                 ♣ 10 6
                    ♠ J
                    ♡ —
                    ◇ 10 7
                    ♣ Q 5 4
```

When Rodwell played the ♠J, West followed with the defenders' last spade. What should declarer throw from dummy? If West began with 4-5-1-3 shape, all dummy's hearts are good and declarer should throw the ♣8. If instead West began with 4-6-1-2 shape, the ♣K is bare and about to fall. In that case the winning discard from dummy is the ♡6. How would you have read the situation?

Rodwell had no difficulty whatsoever in determining the lie of the cards. If West had begun with only five hearts, he would not have discarded one on the second round of diamonds! Not with dummy's ♡AKQxx staring him in the face. 'Throw the low heart,' said Rodwell. The ♣K did indeed fall on the second round and Rodwell had his slam.

Barry Rigal, in his write-up of the deal in the championship bulletin, suggested that West might have made life harder for declarer by discarding a spade on the second round of diamonds. In fact Rigal went further than that, bravely stating that 'Helgemo's actual choice of a heart discard was, in my opinion, a little naïve.' What do you make of that?

A spade discard would have surrendered a trick directly if declarer held something like ♠Q972, so it was far from a cost-free deception. Suppose that West does discard a spade. He will have to find another discard in this position:

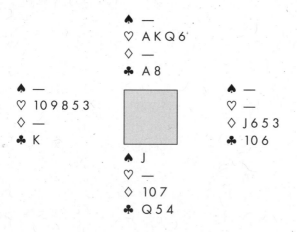

When the ♠J is played, West will give the position away if he throws the ♣K. How will declarer read the position if West throws a heart? Will he conclude that West is throwing from four remaining hearts, with ♡AKQ6 visible in the dummy, to retain a guard on the ♣K? I don't think so.

There is an element of bluff and double-bluff in these positions, of course, and it was an interesting idea of Rigal's that West should discard a spade instead of a heart. I rather think that Rodwell would still have made his slam. Don't you?

ANSWER TO **QUIZ 3** *(page 22)*

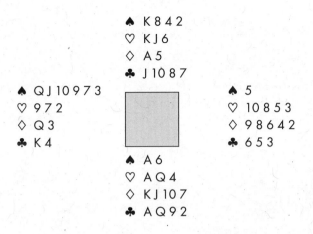

You play in 6NT after West has opened a weak 2♠. You win the ♠Q lead with the ♠A, cross to the ♡J and run the ♣J, losing to West's king. How will you continue when West returns another spade honor?

You win the second spade with dummy's king and play your winners in the round suits before deciding how to play the diamonds. West follows three times in hearts and once more in clubs. All follow to the ♢A and these cards remain:

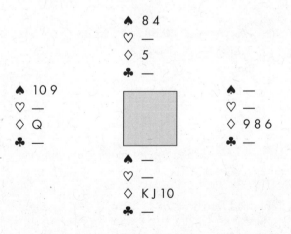

East began with five diamonds to West's two and is therefore a big favorite to hold the ♢Q. However, you need three diamond tricks and if East's remaining three diamonds include the queen, you cannot make the contract! Your only hope is to play a diamond to the king, hoping that West's last diamond is the queen.

Suppose instead that West had started with two hearts and two clubs, leaving him with three diamonds. Since he would need to keep a guard on dummy's ♠8, your last round-suit winner would squeeze him down to a doubleton diamond. Again you would play to drop the ♢Q.

7. BRIDGE BARON'S 6NT

In the 2007 World Computer Bridge Championships, the program Bridge Baron produced a sparkling piece of dummy play in 6NT. Remember, as you watch the play, that Bridge Baron could see only the North and South cards at the time. The East and West cards were being bid and played by two invocations of Shark Bridge, a different computer program. This was the deal:

```
                    ♠ 6
                    ♡ A K Q 8
                    ◇ J 8 4
                    ♣ Q J 10 8 4
 ♠ K Q 8 5 4 2                        ♠ 10 9
 ♡ 7 5           ┌──────────────┐     ♡ J 9 6 4 3 2
 ◇ Q 10 6        │ Neither Vul. │     ◇ 9 5 2
 ♣ 3 2           │ Dealer S     │     ♣ 9 6
                 └──────────────┘
                    ♠ A J 7 3
                    ♡ 10
                    ◇ A K 7 3
                    ♣ A K 7 5
```

West	North	East	South
Shark	Bridge	Shark	Bridge
Bridge	Baron	Bridge	Baron
			1◇
2♠	dbl	pass	3NT
pass	6NT	all pass	

Rough and ready bidding by North-South, you may think, but it was perfectly acceptable for a computer program. How would you play 6NT when West leads the ♠K?

Ducking the opening lead would result in defeat (after a switch to hearts or clubs). Bridge Baron won the first trick with the ♠A and cashed the top cards in clubs and hearts. A diamond to the ace left this end position:

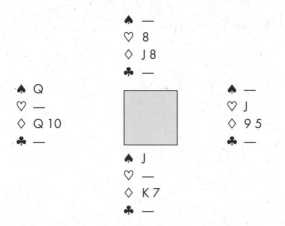

```
                    ♠ —
                    ♡ 8
                    ◇ J 8
                    ♣ —
  ♠ Q                                    ♠ —
  ♡ —              ┌─────────┐           ♡ J
  ◇ Q 10          │         │           ◇ 9 5
  ♣ —              └─────────┘           ♣ —
                    ♠ J
                    ♡ —
                    ◇ K 7
                    ♣ —
```

Dummy's last round-suit winner had already squeezed West out of its second spade winner. Bridge Baron now led the ♠J to West's ♠Q, forcing a lead into the split diamond tenace. Slam made! The play was an example of the strip squeeze, where a defender is squeezed out of a winner and then put on lead.

Suppose West had retained ♠Q8 and bared the ◇Q. Would the Bridge Baron declarer have read the position correctly, playing the ◇K to drop the queen? Only the programmers know the answer! It is likely, of course, that West's weak jump overcall of 2♠ was based on a six-card suit. This is the clue that would allow a human declarer to read the cards correctly and make the slam.

Quiz 4 *How would you play 6NT?*

```
                    ♠ A K 8
                    ♡ 8 5
                    ◇ A 8 6
                    ♣ A 8 7 4 3
  ♡6 led           �════════════
                    ♠ Q 9
                    ♡ K J 9
                    ◇ K Q J
                    ♣ K J 10 6 2
```

West	North	East	South
		2♡	2NT
pass	6NT	all pass	

West leads the ♡6 against your 6NT contract and you win East's ♡10 with the ♡J. What now? **(The answer is overleaf.)**

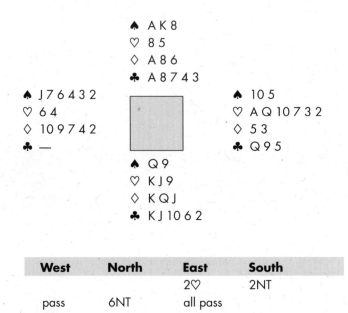

♠ A K 8
♡ 8 5
◇ A 8 6
♣ A 8 7 4 3

♠ J 7 6 4 3 2
♡ 6 4
◇ 10 9 7 4 2
♣ —

♠ 10 5
♡ A Q 10 7 3 2
◇ 5 3
♣ Q 9 5

♠ Q 9
♡ K J 9
◇ K Q J
♣ K J 10 6 2

West	North	East	South
		2♡	2NT
pass	6NT	all pass	

West leads the ♡6 and you win East's ♡10 with the ♡J. What now?

You have seven top tricks outside clubs, so five club tricks will give you the slam. All will be easy when the club suit breaks 2-1; when clubs divide 3-0, you will need to cash the right top honor first. Which of the defenders is more likely to hold three clubs, would you say?

On the evidence currently before you, East probably began with six hearts to West's two and therefore has seven vacant places for clubs to West's eleven. This makes West much more likely than East to hold three clubs. However, there is no need to make the big decision in clubs straight away. You should look first at the lie of the spades and diamonds.

When you play three rounds of diamonds, East shows out on the second round. You continue with three rounds of spades and, once again, East shows out on the second round. So, East's shape is likely to be 2-6-2-3. The only other possibility is that he holds seven hearts and his shape is 2-7-2-2. One thing you know for sure is that he cannot be void in clubs!

You play the ♣A first, certain that this is the right move, and receive your reward when West does indeed show out. You can then finesse the ♣J and claim the contract.

8. THE WORLD'S LUCKIEST 6NT CONTRACT

An exhibition match at the 1998 Summer Congress in Brighton featured two English teams, the Chinese women's team and a team representing Australia. This was the most spectacular deal:

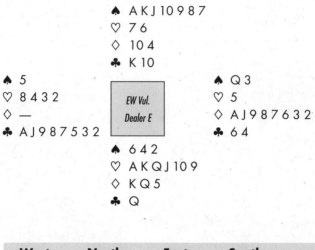

West	North	East	South
Fawcett	Forrester	Burn	Hackett
		3◊	3NT
4♣	6NT	all pass	

Tony Forrester was not inclined to bid 6♠, since in that contract he might suffer a minor-suit ruff. He chose 6NT, hoping that this would be safer. It was indeed entirely safe, but only because the diamonds broke 8-0! Joe Fawcett led the ♣A but had no diamond to play. Paul Hackett won the next trick and soon claimed the contract.

You might expect to gain a few IMPs after making such a lucky slam. At the other table Jason Hackett opened 3◊ on the East cards and the bidding continued 3♡ (South), 4♣ (Justin Hackett, West). North bid 4♠ and Jason contested with 5◊, apparently reading partner's 4♣ as fit-showing. That was minus 1100 and, much to their father's disappointment, 3 IMPs away.

In the other match, Jim Wallis (sitting South for Australia) preferred to bid 4♡ over East's 3◊. When his partner advanced to 4♠, he asked for aces and then bid 6NT. This picked up 11 IMPs when compared against the sober 4♠ contract reached by the Chinese women. Rough justice, indeed!

9. NIELS KROEJGAARD'S 6NT

Denmark's Niels Kroejgaard sat South on this Mixed Pairs deal from the inaugural (2003) European Open Championship, played in Menton.

```
                        ♠ 6
                        ♡ A J 3
                        ◇ A K Q J 4 3 2
                        ♣ A 10
       ♠ Q 3 2                           ♠ J 9 7 5 4
       ♡ 9 8 7 6 4      Both Vul.        ♡ K Q 5
       ◇ 8 7 5          Dealer N         ◇ —
       ♣ 9 4                             ♣ K 7 6 5 2
                        ♠ A K 10 8
                        ♡ 10 2
                        ◇ 10 9 6
                        ♣ Q J 8 3
```

West	North	East	South
	Sand		Kroejgaard
	1◇	pass	1♠
pass	3◇	pass	3NT
pass	4NT	pass	6NT
all pass			

How would you play 6NT when West leads the ♡9?

It was an annoying opening lead for Kroejgaard, since after any other attack he could simply have given up a club trick. How should he attempt to recover after a heart lead? Suppose he ducks a heart at trick 1. Since East cannot safely return a heart, it may seem that declarer needs only to guess who holds the ♣K. If West holds it, a club finesse will suffice. If East holds the ♣K, declarer can cash dummy's ♣A and run the diamonds, followed by the top spades, squeezing East in hearts and clubs.

The flaw in that argument is that when East holds the ♣K he can return a spade to prevent the squeeze. (Declarer would no longer be able to cash dummy's diamonds before reaching and playing the intended squeeze card — the second top spade in the South hand.) Indeed, if any respectable East were to win a ducked heart and switch to a diamond, you should incline towards a club finesse.

Knowing from the opening lead that East held both the missing heart honors, Kroejgaard rose with dummy's ♡A on the first trick. He then ran all seven of dummy's diamonds, throwing the ♠8 and the ♣QJ8. Note the unblock of the two club honors. He cashed one of his spade winners to leave this position:

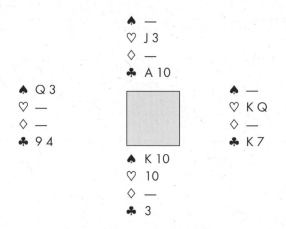

♠ —
♥ J 3
♦ —
♣ A 10

♠ Q 3   ♠ —
♥ —   ♥ K Q
♦ —   ♦ —
♣ 9 4   ♣ K 7

♠ K 10
♥ 10
♦ —
♣ 3

Kroejgaard led the ♠K, throwing the ♡3 from dummy. Sensing a throw-in if she were to release a heart honor, East discarded the ♣7. Should declarer now finesse against West or play to drop the bare king with East? Yes, yes, I realize that you are not blind and can see the right answer from the diagram! Which of the two plays is with the odds, do you think?

You know East began with five clubs to West's two. Even though West still has his two clubs and East is down to one club, the odds remain at '5-to-2 on' that East has the ♣K. Kroejgaard duly played a club to the ace and the slam was his.

Quiz 5 *How would you play 6NT?*

♠ A K Q J 8 3
♥ 8 6
♦ K Q 10
♣ 5 4

♢9 led

♠ 2
♥ K 10 9 7
♦ A J
♣ A K Q J 3 2

West	North	East	South
	1♠	pass	3♣
3♡	4♠	pass	4NT[1]
pass	5♦	pass	6NT
all pass			

(1) Simple Blackwood.

You win the diamond lead with the ace and play the ♣A, West discarding a diamond. When you play dummy's ♠AK, West shows a singleton ♠9. What now? **(The answer is overleaf.)**

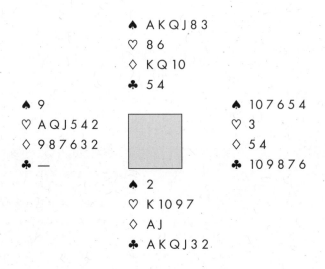

This deal was composed for a Par Contest by Terence Reese and Skid Simon many decades ago. West, who overcalled 3♡, leads the ◇9 against 6NT. You win with the ◇A and play the ♣A, preparing to claim, but West shows out on the first round of clubs, throwing a diamond. When you take a look at the spade suit, West follows with the ♠9 on the first round and then shows out on the second round. What did you expect in a Par Contest, good breaks? How will you recover the situation?

The answer is to cash your remaining two winners in the diamond suit. On the third round of diamonds, East is pressed for a discard:

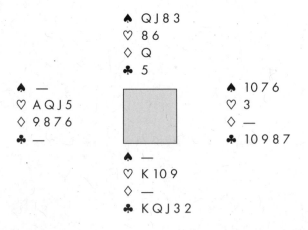

When dummy's ◇Q is played, East cannot discard a spade or a club or he will set up that suit for you. He therefore has to throw his singleton heart. You can then play your remaining club winners and throw East in with the fifth round of clubs. East has nothing but ♠1076 in his hand and has to lead into dummy's ♠QJ8.

10. SAM LEV'S LEAD AGAINST 6NT

In the auction preceding the 2001 Cavendish Pairs, the top four prices were paid for Kwiecien and Pszczola ($46K), Levin and Weinstein ($44K), Chemla and Lévy ($40K) and Helgemo and Lev ($38K). On this deal from the second day of the event, Geir Helgemo and Sam Lev faced Abécassis and Quantin of France.

```
                    ♠ 8 6 4 3 2
                    ♡ Q 6 3
                    ◇ 5 4
                    ♣ K Q 4
  ♠ J 10 5                            ♠ Q 9 7
  ♡ K J 10 9 7       EW Vul.          ♡ 8 5 2
  ◇ J 7 6           Dealer W          ◇ 10 8 2
  ♣ 10 5                              ♣ J 9 8 7
                    ♠ A K
                    ♡ A 4
                    ◇ A K Q 9 3
                    ♣ A 6 3 2
```

West	North	East	South
Lev	Abécassis	Helgemo	Quantin
pass	pass	pass	2◇
pass	2♡	pass	2NT
pass	3♡	pass	3♠
pass	4NT	pass	6◇
pass	6NT	all pass	

Jean-Christophe Quantin's 2◇ was an artificial game-force and (who would have guessed it?) he eventually came to rest in 6NT. Over now to Sam Lev in the West seat. What should he lead?

Lev was not a happy man. The opponents had bid a slam after a limited auction and both their five-card suits (spades and diamonds) were breaking 3-3. The slam would surely be made and a potentially huge cross-IMPed minus score would result for his partnership. Diagnosing the need for some spectacular move, Lev made the normally unthinkable lead of the ♡J — leading from a king into the game-force hand!

Since players at this level would not normally dream of leading from a king after such an auction, Quantin was convinced that East held the ♡K. In that case he would need a 3-3 diamond break, accompanied by either a 3-3 club break or a heart-club squeeze against East (the defender known to hold the ♡K). Quantin rectified the count by allowing the ♡J to win. He won the ♠J switch and ran the diamonds, followed by his remaining spade winner. This position was reached:

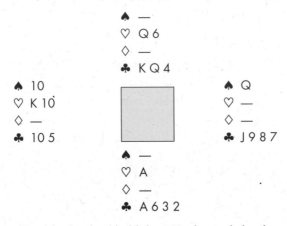

```
              ♠ —
              ♡ Q 6
              ◇ —
              ♣ K Q 4
♠ 10                        ♠ Q
♡ K 10                      ♡ —
◇ —                         ◇ —
♣ 10 5                      ♣ J 9 8 7
              ♠ —
              ♡ A
              ◇ —
              ♣ A 6 3 2
```

If Helgemo (East) had indeed held the ♡K, alongside his four clubs, he would have been squeezed already in this position. To keep four clubs, he would have had to bare the ♡K and that card would then fall under declarer's ♡A.

Quantin cashed the ♡A, barely believing it when East discarded the ♠Q. The clubs did not break and he was one down. Lev and Helgemo picked up an enormous swing and eventually finished sixth in the event, giving their backers an acceptable $57K return on their $38K investment. The top-priced Polish pair won the event, meanwhile, their backers collecting a handsome $228K.

Quiz 6 *How would you play 6NT?*

```
              ♠ Q 9 7
              ♡ A Q 8 7
              ◇ 7 6
              ♣ J 9 8 4
♣6 led
              ♠ K 3
              ♡ K 3 2
              ◇ A K 5
              ♣ A K Q 10 2
```

West	North	East	South
2♠	pass	pass	dbl
pass	3♡	pass	4NT
pass	5◇	pass	6NT
all pass			

North's 3♡ shows 8-10 points. (He is playing the Lebensohl convention and would respond 2NT with 0-7 points.) West leads the ♣6 against your eventual contract of 6NT. What is your plan? **(The answer is on page 36.)**

11. TONY FORRESTER'S 6NT

Tony Forrester sat South on the deal below, from the 1984 Camrose trials. (The Camrose Trophy is contested by the countries of the British Isles).

```
                    ♠ K 4
                    ♡ A Q 3
                    ◇ K 9 8
                    ♣ A 9 5 4 3
  ♠ 9 5                              ♠ Q J 10 8 7 3 2
  ♡ J 9 8 7 6 5 2   ┌─────────┐      ♡ —
  ◇ Q 10 6         │ NS Vul. │      ◇ J 7 3
  ♣ 7              │ Dealer N│      ♣ Q 8 2
                    └─────────┘
                    ♠ A 6
                    ♡ K 10 4
                    ◇ A 5 4 2
                    ♣ K J 10 6
```

West	North	East	South
	Brock		Forrester
	1◇	3♠	3NT
pass	6NT	all pass	

West led the ♠9 and Forrester won in his hand with the ♠A. He could count seven top tricks outside the club suit and therefore needed to guess the club position to bring his total to twelve. Suppose you had been the declarer. How would you have given yourself the best chance in clubs?

The standard first move on such deals is to play on the other suits, gathering as much information as you can about the distribution. At Trick 2 Forrester ducked a round of diamonds. Do you see the point of this? It would enable him to play a total of three rounds of diamonds, aiding his attempt to count the hand.

Forrester won the spade return and played the ♡A, finding that East was void in the suit. Both defenders followed to the ◇A, so declarer knew that East must hold at least two clubs. If East held all four clubs, two red-suit entries to dummy would be required to collect five club tricks. The next move was therefore a club to the ace. (If West had shown out, declarer could finesse the ♣J, return to the ◇K, finesse the ♣10 and cash the ♣K. He would still have the ♡Q as an entry to the fifth club.)

All followed to the first round of clubs and it was now safe to cash the ◇K. Both defenders followed and the count was complete. East's shape was 7-0-3-3 and Forrester duly played a club to the jack. Five club tricks were his — and the slam.

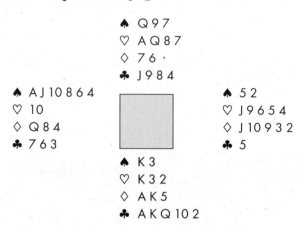

West opens 2♠ and leads the ♣6 against your eventual contract of 6NT. There are ten tricks on top and an easy eleventh available in spades. To score a twelfth trick, you must either find hearts 3-3 or set up a squeeze.

Leading a low card through West's ♠A would not assist you at all. In fact, you want West to score an early spade trick, to rectify the count. So, after winning the club lead you should play the ♠K from your hand. West has to capture, otherwise you would lead towards the ♠Q for a second spade trick. Let's say that West returns the ♠J, won with dummy's ♠Q. Since West holds the sole guard against dummy's ♠9, you will not mind now if East turns up with a heart guard. In that case no one will be able to retain a diamond guard and a double squeeze will result.

You cash three more rounds of clubs, leaving these cards still out:

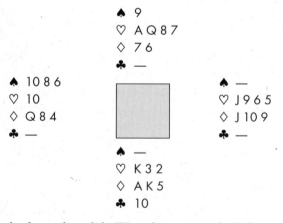

When you lead your last club, West throws a spade and you can spare a diamond from dummy. Since East has to retain four hearts, he releases his diamond guard. You continue with the ♡K, ♡A and ♡Q and now it's West who is squeezed. To keep the ♠10, West has to throw a diamond too. Both defenders have been squeezed out of their diamond guard and your ◇AK5 are good.

12. EDUARDO SCANAVINO'S 6NT

Argentina faced New Zealand in the 1985 Bermuda Bowl. Eduardo Scanavino, an automatic choice for Argentina in those days, sat South on this deal:

```
                 ♠ K Q J 5 4
                 ♡ J 2
                 ◇ 7
                 ♣ A 8 7 6 2
    ♠ 10 8 6                        ♠ 7 3
    ♡ A Q 6 4    Neither Vul.       ♡ 10 8 7 5
    ◇ K 9 6 5 2   Dealer W          ◇ 10 8 4 3
    ♣ J                             ♣ Q 9 5
                 ♠ A 9 2
                 ♡ K 9 3
                 ◇ A Q J
                 ♣ K 10 4 3
```

West	North	East	South
Wright	*Camberos*	*Mayer*	*Scanavino*
pass	1♠	pass	2NT
pass	3♣	pass	3◇
pass	3♠	pass	6NT
all pass			

The bidding table does not tell all! West's opening 'pass' promised the values for a normal opening bid of 1◇. (Some opening bids of 1◇ are more normal than others, it is true.) The Argentinians discovered a club fit but Scanavino could not afford North to become declarer since a heart lead might then give the defenders two quick tricks. Feeling obliged to bid a slam of some sort, he chose 6NT as the final resting place. How would you play this contract when West leads the ♣J?

   With only 12 points missing, and West holding the values for an opening bid, the declarer might have been forgiven had he played West for ♣QJ doubleton. No, he had noticed that the New Zealanders sometimes made their conventional 'pass' quite light. After winning the opening lead with the ♣A, he finessed the ♣10 successfully. Declarer could then count five tricks in each black suit, with the ◇A bringing his total to eleven. He ran his black-suit tricks to reach this end position, with the lead in dummy:

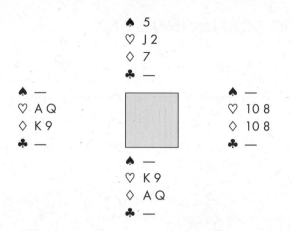

```
              ♠ 5
              ♡ J 2
              ◇ 7
              ♣ —
  ♠ —                      ♠ —
  ♡ A Q                    ♡ 10 8
  ◇ K 9                    ◇ 10 8
  ♣ —                      ♣ —
              ♠ —
              ♡ K 9
              ◇ A Q
              ♣ —
```

When the last black-suit winner was led from dummy, East threw the ♡8 and declarer threw the ♡9. It was not difficult for Lionel Wright (West) to sense the approaching endplay. Instead of reducing to ◇K9 and the ♡A, he chose to bare the ◇K.

Without West's revealing initial pass, this defense might well have beaten the slam. Here, declarer knew that West must hold the ♡A and ♡Q to make up even a light 'opening bid'. Scanavino played a diamond to the ace, dropping West's king, and made his ambitious slam.

Quiz 7 *How would you play 6NT?*

```
              ♠ 9 4
              ♡ A K 9
              ◇ J 7 4
              ♣ A Q 10 6 4
  ♠Q led      ┌──────────┐
              ♠ A K 7 6 3
              ♡ Q 10 5
              ◇ A K Q
              ♣ K 7
```

West	North	East	South
			2NT
pass	6NT	all pass	

How will you play 6NT when West leads the ♠Q? **(The answer is on page 41.)**

13. BILLY EISENBERG'S 6NT

Italy met North America in the final of the 1975 Bermuda Bowl, played in Bermuda, and there was a choice of slams on the deal below. Vito Pittala played in 6♣ for Italy, easily succeeding when the trumps broke 2-2. Billy Eisenberg arrived in 6NT, where life was not so easy.

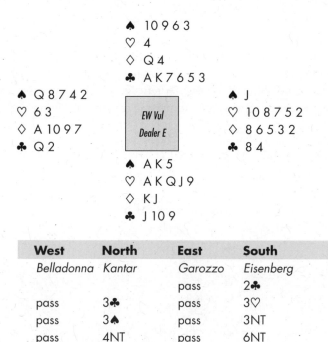

♠ 10 9 6 3
♡ 4
♢ Q 4
♣ A K 7 6 5 3

♠ Q 8 7 4 2   ♠ J
♡ 6 3   ♡ 10 8 7 5 2
♢ A 10 9 7   ♢ 8 6 5 3 2
♣ Q 2   ♣ 8 4

EW Vul
Dealer E

♠ A K 5
♡ A K Q J 9
♢ K J
♣ J 10 9

West	North	East	South
Belladonna	*Kantar*	*Garozzo*	*Eisenberg*
		pass	2♣
pass	3♣	pass	3♡
pass	3♠	pass	3NT
pass	4NT	pass	6NT
all pass			

With no attractive lead, Belladonna placed the ♠4 on the table. Declarer's main chance was to bring in the club suit without loss. Eisenberg noted that four spade tricks (added to five hearts, one diamond and two clubs) were another possible route to success. He therefore played low from dummy, just in case East had started with ♠QJ doubleton. East produced the ♠J and Eisenberg captured with the ♠A.

What next? With three chunky clubs in his hand, there was a serious risk of a blockage in the suit. Playing the ace and king would not be good enough, even if clubs divided 2-2; the remaining card in the South hand would block the suit. Hoping to create an extra entry to dummy, Eisenberg led the ♢K at Trick 2. Belladonna won with the ♢A and smartly returned a diamond, removing the entry before it was of any use.

Eisenberg played three rounds of hearts, discovering the 5-2 break there, and continued with the ♠K. If East had started with ♠QJ doubleton, dummy's ♠10 would have become an extra entry to dummy. East showed out on the second round of spades, however, and everything then depended on bringing in the clubs. How would you have played the suit?

If you play the ♣A (or ♣K) on the first round, you will succeed only when the ♣Q falls singleton. A much better line is to run the ♣J on the first round. This will succeed when West holds the ♣Q, either doubleton or tripleton. You therefore gain in six cases (Q-8-4, Q-8-2, Q-4-2, Q-8, Q-4, Q-2) and lose only in the one case where East holds a singleton ♣Q.

What happened at the table? Eisenberg did indeed plan to run the ♣J on the first round. When he led this card, Belladonna could see that declarer was bound to succeed if he held J-10-x in the suit. If instead he held J-10 doubleton, he must not be allowed to run the jack on the first round. It was just possible that he held J-9-8, which would also cause a blockage. To take advantage of these situations, Belladonna covered the ♣J with the ♣Q. A relieved Eisenberg won with dummy's ♣A, returned to the ♣10 on the second round and re-entered dummy with the ♣K. The slam was his.

Quiz 8 *How would you play 6NT?*

```
                        ♠ 7 5
                        ♡ K Q J 2
                        ◇ A Q J 3
                        ♣ J 7 4
     ♠8 led            ┌──────────────┐
                        └──────────────┘
                        ♠ A J
                        ♡ A 8 3
                        ◇ K 9 5 2
                        ♣ A Q 6 3
```

West	North	East	South
		3♠	3NT
pass	6NT	all pass	

North's 6NT was an overbid. He might have bid 4NT instead, inviting a slam. How will you play 6NT when West leads the ♠8 to East's ♠Q? **(The answer is on page 42.)**

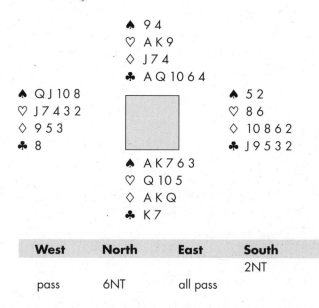

West	North	East	South
			2NT
pass	6NT	all pass	

West leads the ♠Q. You have eleven top tricks and every chance of developing a twelfth trick in clubs. You win the spade lead, cash the ♣K and lead the ♣7. If West follows, you can guarantee the four club tricks that you need by finessing dummy's ♣10. Annoyingly, West shows out on the second club. What now?

You win with dummy's ♣A and must now strip East of his non-clubs, planning to throw him in with a club at Trick 11. Since you need to end in the dummy to perform the throw-in, you must play your spade and diamond winners before the hearts. Both defenders follow to all three diamonds, leaving this position:

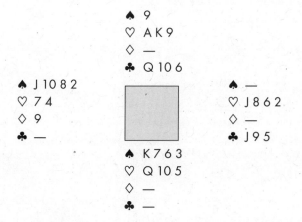

When you play the ♠K, East cannot throw a club or you will set up an extra winner in that suit. He throws the ♡2 and you cash three hearts, ending in the dummy. You then throw East in with the ♣6, forcing a return into the ♣Q-10.

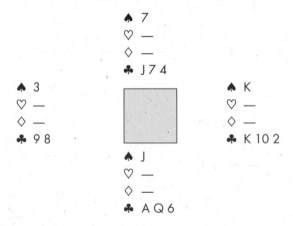

	♠ 7 5		
	♡ K Q J 2		
	◊ A Q J 3		
	♣ J 7 4		

♠ 8 3   ♠ K Q 10 9 6 4 2
♡ 9 7 6 4   ♡ 10 5
◊ 10 8 6 4   ◊ 7
♣ 9 8 5   ♣ K 10 2

	♠ A J		
	♡ A 8 3		
	◊ K 9 5 2		
	♣ A Q 6 3		

West	North	East	South
		3♠	3NT
pass	6NT	all pass	

West leads the ♠8 and you win East's ♠Q with the ace, preserving the option of putting East on lead later. There are only ten tricks on top. Since West is likely to have another spade, you will need East to hold the ♣K to boost your total to eleven. How can you make a twelfth trick? One chance is that East holds a doubleton (or singleton) ♣K, in which case the card will fall.

You cash the red suits, throwing a club from hand. East follows to two hearts and one diamond, throwing five spades including the nine and ten:

	♠ 7		
	♡ —		
	◊ —		
	♣ J 7 4		

♠ 3   ♠ K
♡ —   ♡ —
◊ —   ◊ —
♣ 9 8   ♣ K 10 2

	♠ J		
	♡ —		
	◊ —		
	♣ A Q 6		

Surely West holds the ♠3 and East must have started with 7-2-1-3 shape. You finesse the ♣Q successfully and throw East in with the bare ♠K. He has to lead away from the ♣K and you make two further club tricks for the slam.

Suppose instead East had followed to a second round of diamonds. Counting him for 7-2-2-2 shape, you would have finessed the ♣Q and then cashed the ♣A.

14. THE WORLD'S WORST 6NT CONTRACTS

It is perhaps foolish of me to make such a bold claim in the heading. Emails will arrive: 'You think those 6NT contracts were bad? Just look at what my partner did to me last night. I held...' Well, my first candidate did at least arise in a major tournament — the final of the 2000 Spingold in the USA, with big names occupying all four seats.

```
                  ♠ 7 2
                  ♡ A K Q J 5 2
                  ◇ 4
                  ♣ Q J 8 7
   ♠ 10 8 5 3                        ♠ 6 4
   ♡ 9 3          ┌──────────┐       ♡ 10 8
   ◇ Q 10 6 5 2   │Neither Vul.│     ◇ A K 9 7
   ♣ 9 5          │ Dealer S  │      ♣ A 6 4 3 2
                  └──────────┘
                  ♠ A K Q J 9
                  ♡ 7 6 4
                  ◇ J 8 3
                  ♣ K 10
```

West	North	East	South
Weichsel	*Fredin*	*Sontag*	*Lindkvist*
			1NT
pass	2◇	pass	2♡
pass	2NT	pass	3♣
pass	3♡	pass	3♠
pass	4♣	pass	4♠
pass	6♣	pass	6♠
pass	6NT	dbl	all pass

South's 1NT showed 15-17 points. The 2◇ response showed either spades (weak or invitational) or any hand worth a game force. North's 2NT confirmed the 'game-forcing' type; South's 3♣ asked for North's long suit and 3♡ showed a heart suit. At this point the auction appears to have veered off the rails, ending (as many such auctions do) in 6NT.

Not only were Fredin and Lindkvist completely bare in one suit, they were missing another ace as well! Alan Sontag ventured a double and if West had led a minor suit, the slam would have gone five down. No, Peter Weichsel led a 'safe' heart and declarer escaped for just one down.

At the other table, somewhat surprisingly, Lou Stansby and Chip Martel also reached a slam. They bid to 6♡ and Brad Moss (East) doubled. North-South adjusted the contract to 6♠, putting West on lead, and this time Moss did not double. Placing his partner with heart values as a consequence, Fred Gitelman (West) led a heart and the spade slam was made. Life in the fast lane!

If we move back three decades to 1970, to the Easter International Tournament at London's Europa Hotel, we will find an even worse 6NT contract. It was reported by G.C.H. Fox in the *Daily Telegraph* and, as was the practice in those gentlemanly days, the perpetrators were saved from public humiliation by remaining unnamed.

```
                    ♠ Q 10 7 6 4
                    ♡ 5 4
                    ◇ 8 7 6 5 3
                    ♣ 3
    ♠ 3 2                             ♠ —
    ♡ A Q 10 9 8 7    NS Vul.         ♡ J 6
    ◇ 4               Dealer W        ◇ J 10 9 2
    ♣ A K Q 8                         ♣ 10 9 7 6 5 4 2
                    ♠ A K J 9 8 5
                    ♡ K 3 2
                    ◇ A K Q
                    ♣ J
```

West	North	East	South
1♡	pass	pass	2♡
3♡	3♠	pass	4◇
pass	5◇	pass	6NT
dbl	all pass		

South entered with a 2♡ cuebid, which in those days showed an unspecified game force. When his partner made a free bid in spades, visions of a slam appeared before South's eyes. Perhaps a cuebid of 4◇ would work well. Er… not exactly. North read the bid as natural (why not, indeed?) and raised to game in diamonds.

South bid 6NT with the intention of protecting his ♡K from the opening lead; a thoughtful move, yes, but not particularly brilliant because there were likely to be two aces missing. West doubled and played four rounds of clubs. East overtook on the fourth round and scored his remaining clubs, thereby scoring four defensive tricks more than he had expected. He then switched to the ♡J, allowing the defenders to score all thirteen tricks for a penalty of 3500.

'It's cheaper if you let them play in 1♡,' North observed.

15. ESCAPING INTO 6NT

When a suit slam is doubled, it is not uncommon for the doubled side to seek refuge in 6NT. Sometimes it will be a Lightner Double, made in the hope of attracting a killing lead. On other occasions, the double will be based on a trump stack. If the rescue contract of 6NT proves successful, the perpetrator of the double may be haunted by the deal for a long while. In this chapter we will see a trio of deals where a doubled suit slam was removed to 6NT.

When Greece faced Russia in the 1996 Olympiad, both North-South pairs had to judge how to react to an adverse Lightner Double. This was the layout:

```
                    ♠ A 2
                    ♡ A Q J 7 3 2
                    ◇ K 7 6 4
                    ♣ 7
      ♠ 8 7                           ♠ Q J 10 9 6 5 3
      ♡ 9 8 6 5      Both Vul.        ♡ —
      ◇ Q 5         Dealer S          ◇ 3 2
      ♣ Q 8 5 4 2                     ♣ A K J 9
                    ♠ K 4
                    ♡ K 10 4
                    ◇ A J 10 9 8
                    ♣ 10 6 3
```

West	North	East	South
			1◇
pass	1♡	4♠	pass
pass	4NT	pass	5◇
pass	6◇	dbl	?

The bidding was similar at both tables, with East making a Lightner Double to suggest a lead of dummy's first-bid suit (hearts). What action do you think North-South should take at this point?

The Russian and Greek North-South pairs chose different actions and a swing of 22 IMPs resulted! The Russian South passed and his partner adjusted the contract to 6♡. East doubled again and North redoubled. The diamonds were duly picked up and, after a brief calculation, a score of 2070 was entered in the Russian plus column.

The Greek South liked the look of his ♠K4, poised over the vulnerable 4♠ bid. Instead of passing, as his counterpart had done at the other table, he corrected the contract to 6NT. Switch North's black suits, giving him a more likely hand than his actual one, and this would have been just the right spot. The notrump slam would also have had some chance if West had been on lead, since he might have led a spade rather than a club. No, North's RKCB 4NT bid meant that East was on lead. He doubled 6NT and led a top club, the defenders taking the first five tricks. That was another 1100 for the Russians. I think I would have bid 6NT on those South cards myself. Unlucky!

On to our next exhibit: Germany faced Egypt in the round robin stage of the 2000 World Team Olympiad, and Dirk Schroeder sat South on this deal:

```
                    ♠ A K Q 4
                    ♡ J 6 4
                    ◇ 7 5
                    ♣ A J 6 2
  ♠ 9 6 3                            ♠ 10 8 7
  ♡ K Q 8 7 2        NS Vul.         ♡ —
  ◇ 8 4 3           Dealer E         ◇ K 10 9 6
  ♣ Q 3                              ♣ 10 9 8 7 5 4
                    ♠ J 5 2
                    ♡ A 10 9 5 3
                    ◇ A Q J 2
                    ♣ K
```

West	North	East	South
	Marsal		Schroeder
		pass	1♡
pass	1♠	pass	2◇
pass	3♣	pass	3♠
pass	4♡	pass	4NT
pass	5♡	pass	6♡
dbl	pass	pass	6NT
dbl	all pass		

North's sequence to the heart game, via the fourth suit, suggested that he had values to spare for a game bid, perhaps a hand of 15 or 16 points. Schroeder took up the baton and carried the bidding to 6♡. A disbelieving West found himself staring at ♡KQ872. Should he double the slam or not?

South surely holds the ♡A, for his ambitious bidding, so it is not particularly likely that North-South can make 6NT. In any case, it is by no means certain that they will run in that direction. It is hard to say whether a double of 6♡ is right or wrong. Such doubles tend to be judged solely on their success, or otherwise!

When West did double the heart slam, Schroeder concluded that the heart suit was adversely placed and amended the contract to 6NT. In the way that players do, the Egyptian West doubled again. How would you play this contract when West leads the ♣Q?

With three club tricks assured, Schroeder could count eleven top tricks on the necessary assumption that the ◇K was onside. For a twelfth trick, he aimed to strip West of his non-hearts and then endplay him in that suit. He won with the ♣K, crossed to a spade and took a successful diamond finesse. He then cashed his five remaining black-suit tricks, throwing two hearts and the ◇2. A diamond to the jack won the next trick and he cashed the ◇A.

Schroeder's last three cards were ♡A109. West, who was not looking too pleased with proceedings, was down to ♡KQ8. Declarer led the ♡9 from his hand, won with West's ♡Q, and claimed the last two tricks on the enforced heart return. That was +1680, against the +620 scored by the Egyptian South in four hearts. West's double of the doomed heart slam had proved horrendously expensive, costing his side a net loss of at least 26 IMPs.

Before we pull a discreet curtain over the deal, do you see a second way that 6NT might have been made? Suppose you win the club lead and, realizing how the heart suit must lie, concede a heart trick to West. This rectifies the count and East can be caught subsequently in a minor-suit squeeze. (You will need to take one diamond finesse and cash the ♡A — a Vienna Coup — before running dummy's black-suit winners).

On Round 9 of the 2005 World Transnational Teams, played in Estoril, Gunnar Hallberg sat South on this deal:

```
                    ♠ A J 10 8 6
                    ♡ K Q 10 8
                    ◇ A J 9
                    ♣ K
    ♠ 9 7 5                          ♠ Q 4 2
    ♡ —           Both Vul.          ♡ A J 4 3 2
    ◇ 10 8 4 3 2  Dealer N           ◇ 5
    ♣ Q J 5 4 3                      ♣ 9 8 7 6
                    ♠ K 3
                    ♡ 9 7 6 5
                    ◇ K Q 7 6
                    ♣ A 10 2
```

West	North	East	South
			Hallberg
	1♠	pass	2◇
pass	2♡	pass	4♡
pass	5◇	pass	6♡
pass	pass	dbl	6NT
dbl	all pass		

When East doubled the small slam in hearts, Hallberg took the view that the trump suit was stacked. He corrected the contract to 6NT and this was doubled by West. How would you play the doubled slam when West leads the ♣Q?

On the assumption that only one heart trick would be possible, declarer needed to score five spade tricks to make 6NT. A bucketful of IMPs therefore depended on how the spade suit was played. After winning the club lead with dummy's ♣K, Hallberg called for the ♠J and ran the card successfully. When the suit proved to be 3-3, twelve tricks were his.

The commentators at the time expected declarer to play West for the ♠Q and wondered how Hallberg had read the suit correctly. At the 2007 Lederer Trophy in London, I spotted the tall figure of Hallberg in the bar of the Young Chelsea Club. 'I want to ask you about a 6NT contract that you played,' I said, peering up at him. 'You may not remember it.'

'Of course I will!' Gunnar replied. 'I remember all the hands I play.'

When I asked him why he had chosen to play spades that way, he replied that East would not have doubled 6♡ on a stack of hearts unless he held some other value — something that would assist in the defense against 6NT. After West's lead of the ♣Q, this could only be the ♠Q.

Apart from that, suppose that West did hold the ♠Q. With the heart suit assumed to be breaking 0-5, it was quite possible that West would hold four spades to the queen. In that case declarer would not be able to score the five spade tricks that he needed. (A spade-club squeeze would not yield the contract, since declarer would have only ten tricks once a heart trick had been established).

'What about West's double of 6NT?' I persisted. 'Didn't that make you think that West might hold the ♠Q?'

'No, no,' Hallberg replied. 'He was doubling to protect his partner. That was obvious.'

It was a fine piece of card reading on a deal where a huge swing was at stake. I'm glad that Hallberg was the declarer rather than me.

QUIZ 9 *How would you play 6NT?*

```
                    ♠  A Q J 6
                    ♡  5
                    ◇  Q J 6 4
                    ♣  Q J 8 6
      ♠7 led        ▭▭▭▭▭▭
                    ♠  K 10 2
                    ♡  A Q 8
                    ◇  K 3 2
                    ♣  A K 9 7
```

West	North	East	South
2♡	dbl	pass	6NT
all pass			

How will you play 6NT when West leads the ♠7? **(The answer is on page 51.)**

16. LÉON YALLOUZE'S DEFENSE TO 6NT

Léon Yallouze, an Egyptian by birth, sat East on this deal. It was played more than three decades ago in the windy town of Casablanca, on the Moroccan coast. (Is the setting exotic enough for you?)

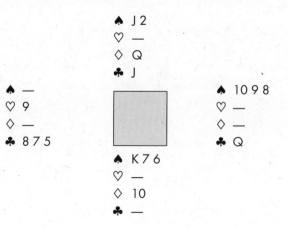

	♠ Q J 2		
	♡ J 10 3		
	♢ A Q 9 3		
	♣ J 10 9		

```
                   ♠ Q J 2
                   ♡ J 10 3
                   ♢ A Q 9 3
                   ♣ J 10 9
  ♠ 5                              ♠ A 10 9 8 3
  ♡ 9 8 7 5         NS Vul.        ♡ 6 4 2
  ♢ 6 5 4          Dealer S        ♢ 7 2
  ♣ 8 7 5 3 2                      ♣ Q 6 4
                   ♠ K 7 6 4
                   ♡ A K Q
                   ♢ K J 10 8
                   ♣ A K
```

West	North	East	South
			2♣
pass	2♢	pass	2NT
pass	6NT	all pass	

Take the East cards and see how you defend the notrump slam. Your partner leads the ♡9, which declarer wins with the ace. He continues with the ♠4, drawing the ♠5 from West and dummy's queen. What is your plan for the defense? If you win this trick, what will you return?

At the other table of this match, East won the first spade and returned a heart. Declarer won and cashed his two top clubs, followed by the remaining red-suit winners. This was the ending, with the lead in dummy:

```
                   ♠ J 2
                   ♡ —
                   ♢ Q
                   ♣ J
  ♠ —                              ♠ 10 9 8
  ♡ 9                              ♡ —
  ♢ —                              ♢ —
  ♣ 8 7 5                          ♣ Q
                   ♠ K 7 6
                   ♡ —
                   ♢ 10
                   ♣ —
```

When the ◇Q was played, East was squeezed in the black suits. Needing to keep the ♣Q to guard against dummy's ♣J, he released a spade. Declarer then scored three spade tricks for his slam.

So, how did Yallouze defend? When a spade was led to dummy's queen, he allowed this card to win. Declarer returned to his hand and played a second round of spades towards dummy's jack (a play that would have landed the slam if West had begun with a doubleton ♠A). West showed out and Yallouze captured dummy's ♠J with the ace. He then returned the ♠10, breaking the spade link between the dummy and declarer's hand. With no link in either black suit, the chance of a squeeze was gone. It was no longer possible to make the slam.

Quiz 10 *How would you play 6NT?*

```
              ♠ A Q 7 6 5 3
              ♡ A 9 4
              ◇ 6 3
              ♣ 7 4
♠10 led       ┌─────────────┐
              └─────────────┘
              ♠ K J 8 4
              ♡ K 7
              ◇ K 10
              ♣ A K Q 8 2
```

West	North	East	South
3◇	3♠	pass	4NT
pass	5♠	pass	6NT
all pass			

To protect the ◇K from the opening lead, you bid the slam in notrump rather than spades. How will you play 6NT when West leads the ♠10? **(The answer is on page 52.)**

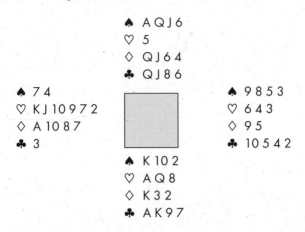

You play in 6NT after West has opened a weak 2♡. He leads the ♠7 and you win with the ♠10. You have nine top tricks outside diamonds, so three tricks from that quarter will give you the slam. Although West might have only four points, your best chance is to play him for the ◇A. By leading low toward dummy's diamond honors on the first two rounds, you can score three diamond tricks when West has a doubleton (or singleton) ◇A, as well as when the suit breaks 3-3. As we will see, you can also succeed when West holds four diamonds to the ace.

At Trick 2 you lead a low diamond, dummy's queen winning. You re-enter your hand with the ♠K and lead a second low diamond towards dummy. You are hoping, of course, that the ◇A will appear from West. No, he disappoints you by following with a spot card and you win with dummy's ◇J. What now?

You play your remaining black-suit winners, reaching this end position:

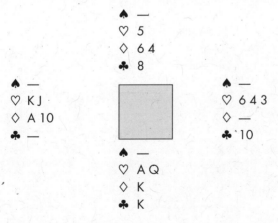

When you play the ♣K, West must bare the ◇A to retain his heart guard. You throw him in with a diamond and he has to lead into your ♡AQ. The three-card ending would be exactly the same if West had started with ◇A87. (If he bares the ♡K instead, you will play the ♡A to drop the king.)

♠ A Q 7 6 5 3
♡ A 9 4
♢ 6 3
♣ 7 4

♠ 10 9   ♠ 2
♡ J 2   ♡ Q 10 8 6 5 3
♢ A Q J 9 8 5 4   ♢ 7 2
♣ 10 3   ♣ J 9 6 5

♠ K J 8 4
♡ K 7
♢ K 10
♣ A K Q 8 2

West	North	East	South
3♢	3♠	pass	4NT
pass	5♠	pass	6NT
all pass			

West leads the ♠10. There are eleven tricks on top and it may seem that you will need a 3-3 club break to make the slam. However, there is an extra chance that East may hold the sole guard on both hearts and clubs. In that case you can catch him in a squeeze without the count. What does that mean? It means that you will not have to concede an early trick (rectifying the count) to set up the squeeze.

You win the spade lead and run the spades, reaching this position:

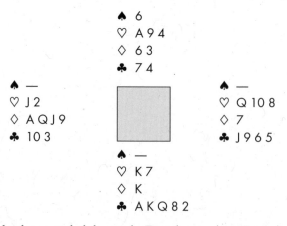

♠ 6
♡ A 9 4
♢ 6 3
♣ 7 4

♠ —   ♠ —
♡ J 2   ♡ Q 10 8
♢ A Q J 9   ♢ 7
♣ 10 3   ♣ J 9 6 5

♠ —
♡ K 7
♢ K
♣ A K Q 8 2

To retain his heart and club guards, East throws the ♢7 on the last spade and you discard the ♢K from your hand. When you play the ♣AKQ East turns up with four clubs. No matter! You give East a club, setting up an extra winner, and he has no diamond to play.

17. JEFF MECKSTROTH'S 6NT

Jeff Meckstroth sat South on this deal from the semi-final of the 1992 Bridge Olympiad, in the Italian spa town of Salsomaggiore Terme. The USA faced Sweden.

```
                    ♠ A K Q 9 2
                    ♡ K 8
                    ◇ K Q 4 3
                    ♣ A 8
    ♠ 10 8                              ♠ J 7 6 3
    ♡ 9 6 3          Neither Vul.       ♡ Q J 10 7
    ◇ J 9 5 2        Dealer N           ◇ 7 6
    ♣ Q 7 5 4                           ♣ J 9 6
                    ♠ 5 4
                    ♡ A 5 4 2
                    ◇ A 10 8
                    ♣ K 10 3 2
```

West	North	East	South
Morath	Rodwell	Bjerregaard	Meckstroth
	1♣	pass	1♡
pass	2♡	pass	2♠
pass	3◇	pass	3♡
pass	3♠	pass	3NT
pass	4◇	pass	4♡
pass	4NT	pass	5♡
pass	6NT	all pass	

The auction is complex, as is often the case with this pair. After the opening forcing club, a series of relays allowed Meckstroth to describe a balanced 11-13 HCP hand, after which both players expressed interest in slam. There is no need for us to worry about the bidding details, however — it's an interesting play hand. How will you tackle the slam when West leads the ♡9?

Meckstroth won the opening lead with dummy's ♡K and played four rounds of spades, setting up an extra spade trick. West, meanwhile, discarded his remaining two hearts. Meckstroth won the heart return with his ace, West throwing a club. He then played the ◇K and ◇A, no jack appearing. The ◇10 was covered by the ◇J and ◇Q, East discarding the ♡10. These cards were still to be played:

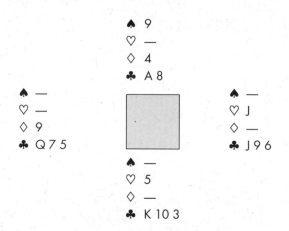

This is the classic matrix of a simultaneous double squeeze. When the ♠9 is played, East has to keep his heart guard and therefore throws a club. Declarer throws the ♡5 from his hand and it is then West's turn to be squeezed. To keep his diamond guard, he too has to throw a club. Declarer can then score three club tricks. At this level, Meckstroth was able to face his cards, mutter 'double squeeze', and there was an immediate concession.

At the other table, the Swedish declarer also reached 6NT but went one down after a different opening lead. A club was led and he won East's ♣J with the ♣K. (West now held sole guard of both minors and could be squeezed if declarer read the cards correctly). When four rounds of spades were played, West threw a heart and a club. Declarer won East's ♡J switch with the ♡K and cashed the ◇K and ◇A, leaving this position:

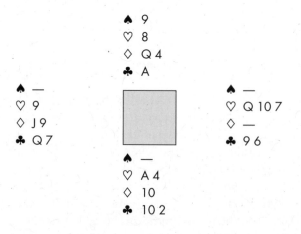

At double-dummy, declarer can now lead the ♣2 to the ♣A, and then cash the ♠9, throwing the ♡4. A heart to the ace would then squeeze West in the minors. It seems that declarer must have read East for the ♣Q, after West's opening lead in the suit. He played a diamond to the queen, testing that suit, and the slam could no longer be made.

18. ZIA MAHMOOD'S 6NT

Zia Mahmood sat South on this deal from the qualifying round of the mixed pairs at the 2002 World Bridge Championships in Montreal.

```
                    ♠ K 3 2
                    ♡ 7 3
                    ◇ A 4
                    ♣ A K Q 10 8 4
♠ 10 9 8 5 4                        ♠ J
♡ A J 10          NS Vul.           ♡ Q 9 8 6 5
◇ J 10 8 2        Dealer N          ◇ Q 9 5
♣ 7                                 ♣ 9 6 3 2
                    ♠ A Q 7 6
                    ♡ K 4 2
                    ◇ K 7 6 3
                    ♣ J 5
```

West	North	East	South
	Radin		Zia
	1♣	pass	1◇
pass	3♣	pass	4♣
pass	4◇	pass	4NT
pass	5◇	pass	6NT
all pass			

How would you play 6NT when West leads the ♠10, East's ♠J appearing?

There are eleven tricks on top. If spades break 3-3 you will have an easy twelfth trick but that can hardly be the case after the cards you have seen at Trick 1. Another obvious chance is that East will hold the ♡A. In that case you can simply lead toward the ♡K. Do you see any other possibility?

Zia was confident, from East's unconsidered and immediate play of the ♠J, that this card was a singleton. He won the first trick in his hand with the ♠A, leaving open the possibility from West's point of view that East held the ♠Q. He then played the ♠6. West contributed the ♠4 and Zia called for dummy's ♠2! East showed out and the slam was then his.

It may seem to you that West was foolish not to cover the ♠6 and that there was nothing to lose by doing so. West should indeed have covered in spades but that would not necessarily be the end of the story. Declarer's remaining ♠Q7 would then be a tenace against West's ♠95. If Zia were to place the ♡A on his left, he could run the minor-suit winners to arrive at this end position:

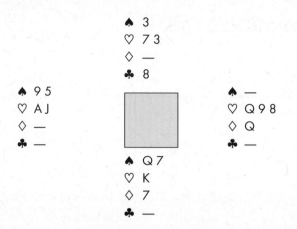

```
              ♠ 3
              ♡ 7 3
              ◇ —
              ♣ 8
♠ 9 5                        ♠ —
♡ A J                        ♡ Q 9 8
◇ —                          ◇ Q
♣ —                          ♣ —
              ♠ Q 7
              ♡ K
              ◇ 7
              ♣ —
```

On dummy's last club winner, Zia would throw the ◇7. West would have little option but to reduce to ♠95 and the ♡A and could then be thrown in with a heart, to lead back into declarer's spade tenace.

There would be no particular reason to play this way, rather than leading toward the ♡K (hoping that East held the ♡A). I will leave it to you to decide whether Zia, the great showman, would have preferred the more spectacular of the two plays!

Quiz 11 *How would you play 6NT?*

```
                         ♠ 9 6 2
                         ♡ 6 4 3
                         ◇ A 8 7 3 2
                         ♣ 5 3
    ♡10 led
                         ♠ A K 3
                         ♡ A J
                         ◇ K Q J
                         ♣ A K Q J 10
```

West	North	East	South
			2♣
pass	2◇	pass	4NT
pass	6NT	all pass	

West leads the ♡10, East playing the ♡Q. An overtrick will be easy if diamonds break 3-2. How will you seek twelve tricks against a 4-1 diamond break? **(The answer is on page 59.)**

19. MICHEL ABÉCASSIS' 6NT

In the 2000 Cavendish Pairs, Michel Abécassis and Jean-Christophe Quantin of France faced Brad Moss of the USA and Fred Gitelman of Canada. Abécassis sat South on the following deal:

```
                    ♠ K 9 3
                    ♡ Q J 7
                    ◇ A 7 4
                    ♣ 10 6 4 3
  ♠ Q 5 4 2                        ♠ J 8 6
  ♡ 2             Neither Vul.     ♡ 10 9 8 5 4 3
  ◇ 8 6 2         Dealer N         ◇ J 5 3
  ♣ J 9 8 7 2                      ♣ Q
                    ♠ A 10 7
                    ♡ A K 6
                    ◇ K Q 10 9
                    ♣ A K 5
```

West	North	East	South
Moss	Quantin	Gitelman	Abécassis
	pass	pass	2♣
pass	2◇	pass	2NT
pass	6NT		

What lead should Brad Moss choose against 6NT, would you say? Leading a major suit would be too dangerous, but the decision between the minors is close. How about a club? You would not normally lead from an honor, but the fact that you have five cards in the suit makes the lead safer than if you held four cards. (The longer the opening leader's holding, the shorter declarer's and dummy's holdings are likely to be. Declarer will therefore have less potential for scoring an extra trick in the suit.) Rightly or wrongly, Moss chose to lead a low club; as it happens, this gave nothing away.

Abécassis won East's ♣Q with the ♣A, cashed the ♣K and led another club. Moss won with the ♣J and returned a fourth round of clubs, East throwing three hearts meanwhile. Declarer discarded the ♠10 on the fourth round of clubs. Undecided as to how to play the diamonds, he then cashed his three heart winners. These cards remained:

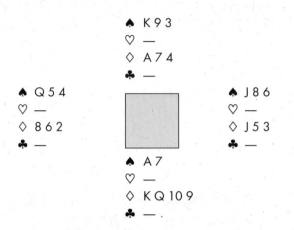

```
                    ♠ K 9 3
                    ♡ —
                    ◇ A 7 4
                    ♣ —
    ♠ Q 5 4                          ♠ J 8 6
    ♡ —                              ♡ —
    ◇ 8 6 2                          ◇ J 5 3
    ♣ —                              ♣ —
                    ♠ A 7
                    ♡ —
                    ◇ K Q 10 9
                    ♣ — .
```

Seeking further information before making his key play in diamonds, Abécassis next played the ♠K and ♠A. Brad Moss, in the West seat, was aware of what was going on. On the second round of spades he dropped the ♠Q, hoping to give the impression that he held ◇Jxxx!

Did Abécassis go down now? He did not. He played diamonds from the top and made his slam. Why do you think he played this way?

I have no phone or email contact with Monsieur Abécassis and, like you, will therefore have to guess what thoughts were running through the Frenchman's mind. First of all, let's evaluate the situation on the basis that West's ♠Q on the second round is a true card (from either ♠Q4 or ♠QJ4). The Principle of Restricted Choice makes ♠Q4 a 2-to-1 favorite. Since this implies that West will hold four diamonds to East's two, should you therefore run the ◇10 on the first round? The first round finesse will win two times out of three when West holds four diamonds but it will lose half the time when diamonds are 3-3 (when East holds ◇Jxx). The alternative line, playing for the drop, will win when diamonds are 3-3 or one defender holds ◇Jx. In fact, running the ◇10 gives you a 61% chance — a slight edge over playing for the drop, which gives you a 56% chance.

However, it is far from certain that West's ♠Q is a true card. If he did begin with ♠Q4, East has chosen to play the ♠6 and the ♠8 from ♠J865! Since few defenders would have dropped these particular cards from such a combination, there is a huge bias toward East holding ♠J86. This 'strange choice of spot card' phenomenon is surely enough to overturn the narrow 61-to-56 odds that would apply when the ♠Q is a true card.

When you need to read which cards a particular defender has kept, keep a close watch on the cards played by the other defender. He is less likely to be aware of the need for any deception.

ANSWER TO **QUIZ 11** (*page 56*)

```
                        ♠ 9 6 2
                        ♡ 6 4 3
                        ◇ A 8 7 3 2
                        ♣ 5 3
    ♠ Q J 8 7                             ♠ 10 5 4
    ♡ 10 9 8 7 2                          ♡ K Q 5
    ◇ 5                                   ◇ 10 9 6 4
    ♣ 9 7 6                               ♣ 8 4 2
                        ♠ A K 3
                        ♡ A J
                        ◇ K Q J
                        ♣ A K Q J 10
```

West	North	East	South
			2♣
pass	2◇	pass	4NT
pass	6NT	all pass	

West leads the ♡10 and you win East's ♡Q with the ♡A. If diamonds break 3-2, it will be easy. When diamonds are 4-1, or 5-0, your best chance is a stepping stone squeeze. In other words, you must reduce one of the defenders to his diamond guard and an outside winner. You will then cash the diamonds in your hand and put the defender on lead to give you the final trick with the ◇A.

After winning the heart lead, you cash five rounds of clubs, West throwing two hearts, East throwing two spades. When you continue with the ◇K and ◇Q, West discards a heart on the second round. Now you play the ♠AK:

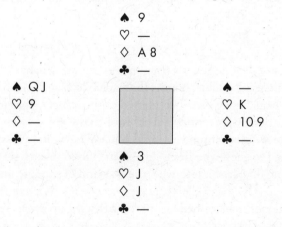

```
                        ♠ 9
                        ♡ —
                        ◇ A 8
                        ♣ —
    ♠ Q J                                 ♠ —
    ♡ 9                                   ♡ K
    ◇ —                                   ◇ 10 9
    ♣ —                                   ♣ —
                        ♠ 3
                        ♡ J
                        ◇ J
                        ♣ —
```

You cash the ◇J and put East on lead with a heart, scoring the ◇A at Trick 13.

If West turned up with four diamonds, you would have to hope that he came down to four diamonds and the bare ♠Q, allowing the same play at the end.

20. GROMOV'S LEAD AGAINST 6NT

This was the penultimate deal of both the 2007 World Transnational Teams final and the Bermuda Bowl final, contested in Shanghai. We will look first at what happened in the Bermuda Bowl.

```
                    ♠ J
                    ♡ A K Q 10 2
                    ◊ A K 10 7 6
                    ♣ Q 10
    ♠ 9 7 6 2                         ♠ A 10 4 3
    ♡ J 8 5 4        EW Vul.          ♡ 7 6 3
    ◊ 8 3            Dealer E         ◊ 9 4 2
    ♣ K 8 5                           ♣ 9 7 6
                    ♠ K Q 8 5
                    ♡ 9
                    ◊ Q J 5
                    ♣ A J 4 3 2
```

West	North	East	South
Rosenberg	Helness	Zia	Helgemo
		pass	1♣
pass	1♡	pass	1♠
pass	2◊	pass	2NT
pass	3◊	pass	4♣
dbl	pass	pass	rdbl
pass	4♡	pass	4♠
pass	4NT	pass	5◊
pass	6NT	all pass	

Geir Helgemo's 4♣ was a cuebid agreeing diamonds as trumps. Michael Rosenberg (West) made a lead-directing double, hoping that a club lead against 6◊ would be beneficial. Indeed it would have been but, alerted to this danger, Tor Helness bid the slam in notrump, thereby preventing a lead through the ♣A.

Rosenberg led the ♠7, Zia winning with the ♠A and returning a club. On the face of it, Helgemo had to guess whether to finesse in clubs or hearts. Deciding to trust the lead-directing double, he rose with the ♣A and eventually finessed the ♡10 to make the slam. (No heart-club squeeze was possible because this would require dummy's diamonds to be cashed before the ♠KQ were played. The entries for this had been destroyed.)

At the other table of the Bowl final, Boye Brogeland sat East for Norway and led a club against Steve Garner's 6◊. Declarer ran the lead to his queen and the Norwegians scored the first two tricks.

Over now to the final of the World Transnational Teams. This was the bidding at the table where Andrei Gromov sat West for Russia/Poland:

West	North	East	South
Gromov	M.Bessis	Dubinin	T.Bessis
		pass	1♣
pass	1♡	pass	1♠
pass	3◊	pass	3NT
pass	4◊	pass	4♠
pass	4NT	pass	5◊
pass	6NT	all pass	

After this auction what would you have led from the West hand against Thomas Bessis's contract of 6NT?

Gromov gave the contract virtually no chance with the brilliantly imaginative lead of the ♡8! Forced into an early decision in the suit, Bessis rose with the ♡A. When he knocked out the ♠A, East switched to a club and the enforced club finesse lost, putting the slam one down. Russia-Poland gained 14 IMPs when Balicki played 6NT from the North seat at the other table and was favored with a heart lead into his tenace.

Quiz 12 *How would you play 6NT?*

```
              ♠ 7 5
              ♡ 5 4
              ◊ 9 7
              ♣ A J 10 9 6 4 2
  ♠J led      ┌──────────┐
              └──────────┘
              ♠ A Q
              ♡ A Q 7
              ◊ A K Q J 8 2
              ♣ K 5
```

West	North	East	South
			2♣
pass	2◊	pass	3NT
pass	6NT	all pass	

West leads the ♠J to your queen. How will you play the slam? **(The answer is overleaf.)**

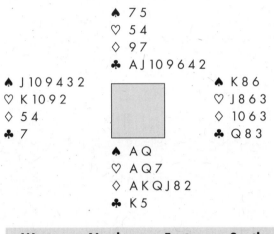

♠ 7 5
♡ 5 4
◇ 9 7
♣ A J 10 9 6 4 2

♠ J 10 9 4 3 2   ♠ K 8 6
♡ K 10 9 2   ♡ J 8 6 3
◇ 5 4   ◇ 10 6 3
♣ 7   ♣ Q 8 3

♠ A Q
♡ A Q 7
◇ A K Q J 8 2
♣ K 5

West	North	East	South
			2♣
pass	2◇	pass	3NT
pass	6NT	all pass	

West leads the ♠J against 6NT and you win with the ♠Q. How will you continue?

You have twelve cards left in your hand and only one of them will now be good enough to leave your slam with a chance. You must play the ♣5. West follows and you play dummy's ♣J. If East wins with the ♣Q, which would be poor defense, you will win his return and make the contract easily by overtaking the ♣K with the ♣A. Let's assume that East was not born yesterday and realizes that he should hold up the ♣Q. What now?

Dummy's ◇97 represents a certain entry to the dummy. You should therefore continue with a low club to the king. West shows out and you next lead the ◇2 to dummy's ◇7. East wins with the ◇10 but you can capture his return and lead the ◇8 to dummy's ◇9 to reach the five good clubs there.

Did you see that there was a way to beat the contract? Suppose West happens to find a diamond lead. This will kill the entry to dummy prematurely. Well, it will if East resists the temptation to cover dummy's ◇9 with the ◇10!

21. ROY WELLAND'S 6NT

USA's Roy Welland sat South on the deal below, from the semi-finals of the mixed teams at the inaugural European Open in 2001.

```
                    ♠ Q 4
                    ♡ K Q 10
                    ◇ K 9 3
                    ♣ A K Q 10 4
   ♠ J 10 8 7 5 2   ┌──────────┐   ♠ K
   ♡ 9 8            │  NS Vul. │   ♡ A J 7 5 4 3
   ◇ Q 10           │  Dealer W│   ◇ 8 6 4 2
   ♣ 9 7 2          └──────────┘   ♣ 6 3
                    ♠ A 9 6 3
                    ♡ 6 2
                    ◇ A J 7 5
                    ♣ J 8 5
```

West	North	East	South
Schaltz	*Levin*	*Blakset*	*Welland*
2◇	dbl	2♠	3NT
pass	6NT	all pass	

West's opening bid was the Multi 2◇, usually based on a weak-two in one of the majors. East's 2♠ response indicated that he was willing to bid higher if West's suit was hearts. In other words, it suggested length in hearts but not spades. What should South bid now?

Relying on partner to provide some cover in hearts, Roy Welland responded 3NT. (Presumably he was playing the Lebensohl convention and could not bid a natural 2NT, although this was not mentioned in the original report.) Jill Levin did not hold back either, leaping straight to 6NT. How would you play this ambitious contract when West leads the ♠J. Note that the East-West convention card states that a jack lead denies a higher honor.

Even if you ignore the opponents' convention card, it is extremely unlikely that West would lead from a KJ10 combination against 6NT. Welland rightly called for a low spade from dummy and was rewarded by the appearance of East's king. He won with the ♠A and led a heart to the king, East ducking.

Four diamond tricks would now give declarer the contract. Welland marked time by playing five rounds of clubs, East throwing three hearts and West two spades. When he played dummy's ◇K, the ◇10 fell from West. These cards remained:

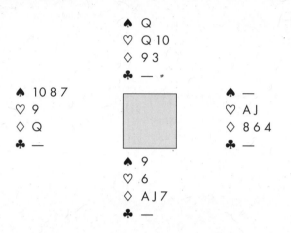

```
              ♠ Q
              ♡ Q 10
              ◇ 9 3
              ♣ —
   ♠ 10 8 7              ♠ —
   ♡ 9                   ♡ A J
   ◇ Q                   ◇ 8 6 4
   ♣ —                   ♣ —
              ♠ 9
              ♡ 6
              ◇ A J 7
              ♣ —
```

Since it was unlikely that West had opened a multi on a 1-count, Welland placed West with an original ◇Q10 doubleton. How should he continue in that case?

Playing dummy's ◇3 to the ◇A would not work — the ◇9 would block the suit on the next round, preventing a finesse of the ◇7. Welland duly led the ◇9 to the ◇A. When West's queen fell, he could return to dummy with the ♠Q and finesse the ◇7 for the contract. Nice effort!

QUIZ 13 *How would you play 6NT?*

```
              ♠ A K J 9
              ♡ A 6
              ◇ A Q 6
              ♣ A 8 5 3
◇J led        ▭
              ♠ Q 7 5
              ♡ K Q 10 5 3
              ◇ K 4
              ♣ J 7 2
```

West	North	East	South
			1♡
pass	1♠	pass	2♠
pass	3♣	pass	3NT
pass	6NT	all pass	

How will you play 6NT when West leads the ◇J? **(The answer is on page 66.)**

22. KRZYSTOF MARTENS' PASS OVER 6NT

The opponents bid to 6NT and you are on lead with the ♣AK, should you double the contract or not? Poland's Krzystof Martens faced such a decision when Poland met India during the 2007 Bermuda Bowl in Shanghai. This was the deal:

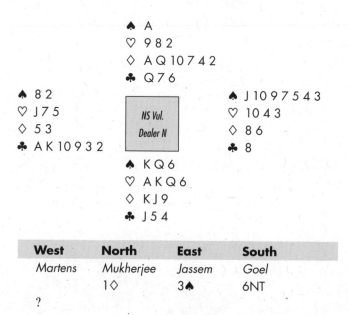

	North		
	♠ A		
	♡ 9 8 2		
	◊ A Q 10 7 4 2		
	♣ Q 7 6		

West		East
♠ 8 2		♠ J 10 9 7 5 4 3
♡ J 7 5	NS Vul.	♡ 10 4 3
◊ 5 3	Dealer N	◊ 8 6
♣ A K 10 9 3 2		♣ 8

	South		
	♠ K Q 6		
	♡ A K Q 6		
	◊ K J 9		
	♣ J 5 4		

West	North	East	South
Martens	Mukherjee	Jassem	Goel
	1◊	3♠	6NT
?			

Displaying no emotion, Martens reached for the green Pass card. Why do you think that was? Was the Polish maestro asleep?

The answer is that he feared such a double might persuade the opponents to run to 7◊. East would be on lead against that contract and might well have to find a club lead in order to defeat the grand slam!

The cards lay exactly as Martens had imagined. Suppose he had doubled and North (or South) had run to 7◊. On any lead but a club from East, declarer would score six diamonds, four hearts and three spades.

The Pole's well-reasoned pass over 6NT paid off in an unexpected way. Kamal Mukherjee took a favorable view of his ♠A and the extra diamond length, making a somewhat undisciplined raise to 7NT. Since a retreat to diamonds was no longer possible, Martens displayed no further reluctance to double. North's advance to the grand slam had cost his side an extra 400 points.

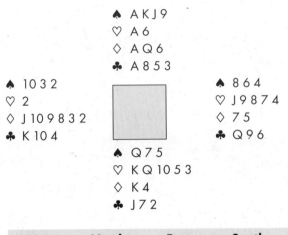

♠ A K J 9
♡ A 6
◇ A Q 6
♣ A 8 5 3

♠ 10 3 2
♡ 2
◇ J 10 9 8 3 2
♣ K 10 4

♠ 8 6 4
♡ J 9 8 7 4
◇ 7 5
♣ Q 9 6

♠ Q 7 5
♡ K Q 10 5 3
◇ K 4
♣ J 7 2

West	North	East	South
			1♡
pass	1♠	pass	2♠
pass	3♣	pass	3NT
pass	6NT	all pass	

West leads the ◇J and you win in your hand with the ◇K. You have eleven tricks on top. What now?

What will happen if you give the matter little thought and continue with the ♡A and ♡K? West will show out on the second round and there will be no way to recover. (Your best hope would be to cash two more diamonds and three spades. If East began with the ♣K and ♣Q, he would have to keep ♡J9 ♣KQ6. You could then endplay him with a low club toward your ♣J72. After winning, he would have to lead one of your two tenaces.)

There is no need to worry about such a tricky recovery operation, which would in any case require a very fortunate club position. When East follows to the second round of hearts, you simply insert the ♡10. If the finesse loses to West's ♡J the suit is breaking 4-2 at worst and you will have your twelfth trick. When the cards lie as in the diagram, the finesse will win and again you will have twelve tricks available.

Suppose instead that East shows out on the second round of hearts. You would win with the ♡K and play your winners in spades and diamonds. Your aim would be to endplay West with a club, forcing him to lead into your heart tenace.

23. DAN MORSE'S 6NT

The 1998 Generali World Masters tournament, contested in Corsica, was preceded by a two-session teams event. The USA's Dan Morse sat South on this deal playing for WBF-2 against China.

```
                        ♠ 7 5
                        ♡ A J 10 6 3
                        ◇ J 10 4
                        ♣ Q 6 4
      ♠ K J 10 9 6 4 2            ♠ 3
      ♡ Q 9 4 2       ┌─────────┐  ♡ 8 7
      ◇ —            │Neither Vul.│ ◇ Q 9 8 7 5 3
      ♣ J 10         │ Dealer S  │  ♣ 9 8 7 2
                     └─────────┘
                        ♠ A Q 8
                        ♡ K 5
                        ◇ A K 6 2
                        ♣ A K 5 3
```

West	North	East	South
Sun Ming	Wignall	Wang Wenfei	Morse
			2♣
2♠	dbl	pass	2NT
pass	3♡	pass	3NT
pass	4NT	pass	6NT
all pass			

John Wignall's first-round double was negative, indicating some values. How would you have played the notrump slam when West leads the ♣J?

Morse won the club lead in his hand, cashed the ♡K and finessed the ♡J successfully. When he continued with the ♡A, throwing the ♠8 from hand, East discarded a diamond. Morse continued with a fourth round of hearts, discarding the ♠Q and setting up a long heart in dummy. Sun Ming, sitting West, was on lead in this position:

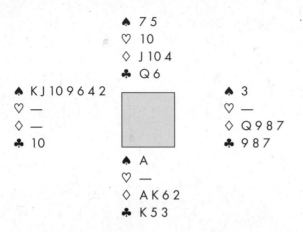

```
              ♠ 7 5
              ♡ 10
              ◇ J 10 4
              ♣ Q 6
♠ K J 10 9 6 4 2              ♠ 3
♡ —                           ♡ —
◇ —                           ◇ Q 9 8 7
♣ 10                          ♣ 9 8 7
              ♠ A
              ♡ —
              ◇ A K 6 2
              ♣ K 5 3
```

How would you continue when West exits safely with the ♣10?

Suppose you win with dummy's ♣Q, maintaining fluidity in that suit. Your aim is to squeeze East in the minor suits but what will happen if you play the squeeze card (dummy's ♡10) at this stage? East will not be squeezed because the ♠3 is available as a safe discard!

Morse made no such mistake. He won the club continuation in his hand, with the king. He then cashed the ♠A, removing East's last spare card. He returned to dummy with the ♣Q and the time was then right to play dummy's thirteenth heart. East had to surrender an extra trick in one of the minor suits and the slam was made.

Quiz 14 *How would you play 6NT?*

```
              ♠ 9 7 5 4
              ♡ K 7 5 3
              ◇ A 4
              ♣ 5 4 2
♣Q led        
              ♠ A K
              ♡ A Q
              ◇ K Q 8 6 3 2
              ♣ A K 7
```

West	North	East	South
			2♣
pass	2◇	pass	3NT
pass	6NT	all pass	

How will you play the slam when West leads the ♣Q? **(The answer is on page 72.)**

24. ESCAPING FROM 6NT

Not many pages ago, we admired Krzystof Martens' refusal to double 6NT when he was on lead with an ace-king combination. Not all bridge players possess such restraint. We will see next a couple of deals where a contract of 6NT was reached and doubled by the defender on lead. Horror of horrors — a rescue to the seven-level then proved successful! The first such deal arose in the 1998 Blue Ribbon Pairs, contested in Nashville:

```
              ♠ A K Q 4
              ♡ A Q 8
              ◇ A Q 8
              ♣ Q 3 2

  ♠ J 8 6 5 3           ┌──────────┐    ♠ 10 9 2
  ♡ K J 9 7 3           │ Both Vul. │    ♡ 10 4 2
  ◇ 10                  │ Dealer E  │    ◇ 6 5
  ♣ 10 8                └──────────┘    ♣ A K 9 7 6

              ♠ 7
              ♡ 6 5
              ◇ K J 9 7 4 3 2
              ♣ J 5 4
```

West	North	East	South
	Coren		Lair
		pass	2◇
pass	6NT	dbl	pass
pass	7◇	all pass	

Mark Lair opened with a weak 2◇ and Richard Coren leapt to 6NT. It was entirely possible that South did not hold the ♣A or ♣K. Unless East happened to hold both of these cards, however, there was a good chance that he would not find a club lead.

When East's double suggested that he was staring at the two top club honors, Coren put the other defender on lead by removing to 7◇. West now had to guess which black suit to lead. When he chose a spade, Lair was in with a chance. He won with dummy's ♠A, drew trumps in two rounds and cashed dummy's other two spade honors, throwing a heart and a club. He then ran the remaining trumps, arriving at this double-squeeze end position:

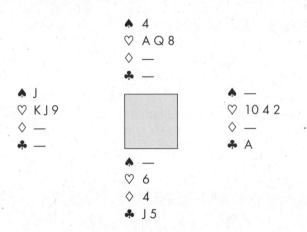

```
                    ♠ 4
                    ♡ A Q 8
                    ◇ —
                    ♣ —
    ♠ J                              ♠ —
    ♡ K J 9        ┌─────────┐      ♡ 10 4 2
    ◇ —            │         │      ◇ —
    ♣ —            └─────────┘      ♣ A
                    ♠ —
                    ♡ 6
                    ◇ 4
                    ♣ J 5
```

When the ◇4 was led, West had to retain his spade guard and therefore discarded the ♡9. Away went dummy's ♠4 and East was similarly squeezed. To retain his club guard, he too had to discard a heart. Declarer then finessed the ♡Q and scored two further heart tricks for his grand slam.

Removing 6NT doubled to an ultimately successful grand slam is not such a rare occurrence as you may think. The second example arose three years later in the same event — the 2001 Blue Ribbon Pairs in Orlando.

```
                    ♠ —
                    ♡ A Q 9 8 3 2
                    ◇ K Q J 10 5 4
                    ♣ 8
    ♠ A K J 4       ┌─────────┐      ♠ Q 9 7 6 3 2
    ♡ 10 7 4        │ EW Vul. │      ♡ K 6 5
    ◇ 7 3 2         │ Dealer S│      ◇ 9 6
    ♣ 10 9 2        └─────────┘      ♣ 6 5
                    ♠ 10 8 5
                    ♡ J
                    ◇ A 8
                    ♣ A K Q J 7 4 3
```

West	North	East	South
Pszczola	Dupont	Zia	Garozzo
			1♣
pass	1♡	pass	3♣
pass	3◇	pass	3NT
pass	6◇	pass	6NT
dbl	pass	pass	7♣
dbl	all pass		

Benito Garozzo might have bid 3♠ at his third turn, enquiring whether partner could provide a spade stopper for 3NT. No, the macho action was to go straight to 3NT. A few seconds later, the auction had reached 6NT. Be honest now. What action would you have taken on Jacek Pszczola's hand?

Visualizing an effective defense against 6NT, Pszczola decided to double. Two passes followed and Garozzo took a second look at the quality of his spade stopper. Concluding that it might not be up to the task, he elected to cut his losses in 7♣, which was also doubled. A top spade was led and Garozzo expressed a heartfelt 'Thank you, partner!' when the dummy went down with a spade void. That was +1630 and a lesson to West — indeed, to us all — that some 'obvious doubles' are a better investment than others.

Quiz 15 *How would you play 6NT?*

```
              ♠ 8 7 6 2
              ♡ A 2
              ♢ Q 8 6
              ♣ A Q 7 6
  ♠K led       ▭▭▭▭▭
              ♠ A 5
              ♡ K Q J 7 5
              ♢ A K 4
              ♣ K 4 2
```

West	North	East	South
			2NT
pass	6NT	all pass	

How will you play 6NT when West leads the ♠K? **(The answer is on page 73.)**

```
                        ♠ 9 7 5 4
                        ♡ K 7 5 3
                        ◇ A 4
                        ♣ 5 4 2
     ♠ J 10 6 2                              ♠ Q 8 3
     ♡ 8 4 2                                 ♡ J 10 9 6
     ◇ 10                                    ◇ J 9 7 5
     ♣ Q J 10 9 3                            ♣ 8 6
                        ♠ A K
                        ♡ A Q
                        ◇ K Q 8 6 3 2
                        ♣ A K 7
```

West	North	East	South
			2♣
pass	2◇	pass	3NT
pass	6NT	all pass	

West leads the ♣Q and down goes the dummy. You see that you need only a 3-2 diamond break to give you thirteen easy tricks. If diamonds do break favorably, you will have to apologize to your team mates for missing the grand slam. Meanwhile, how will you play your modest contract of 6NT?

Suppose you win the club lead, unblock your ♡A and ♡Q and cross to the ◇A. In dummy for the last time, you take the opportunity to cash the ♡K, ditching your club loser. When you play a second round of diamonds to the king, you receive your first piece of bad news. The diamonds fail to break, East holding four cards in the suit. You have no option but to surrender a diamond, to set up two long cards there, but then a truly awful piece of news arrives. When East wins the fourth round of diamonds, he is able to cash the ♡J. You are one down!

That line of play might be a reasonable risk at matchpoints, where the overtrick in 6NT could be valuable. At IMPs or Chicago it would be somewhat careless. To guard against a 4-1 diamond break, you should duck a round of diamonds when it is safe to do so (before you have established a heart winner for the defense). After winning the club lead and cashing the ♡AQ, you should duck the first round of diamonds. Nothing can then prevent you from winning the return and crossing to the ◇A to enjoy the ♡K. The slam is yours.

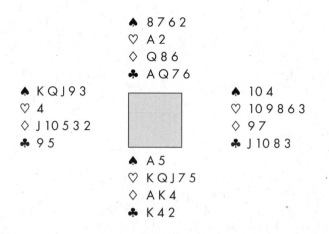

West leads the ♠K. The slam is at risk only when the hearts break 5-1 or 6-0. In that case you will need clubs to divide 3-3, or to squeeze one of the defenders (in hearts and clubs, or perhaps spades and clubs).

To take advantage of these squeeze chances, you must rectify the count. The only practical way to do this is to duck the first trick, allowing West's ♠K to win. You win the spade continuation with the ace and play two rounds of hearts, West discarding a diamond on the second round. Both defenders follow to two rounds of clubs and you apply pressure by cashing your diamond winners. This is the end position:

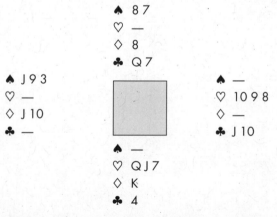

Because you had the foresight to duck the first spade trick, East now has no card to spare when you play the ◊K. Whether he throws a heart or a club, you will have your twelfth trick.

Suppose instead that West had started with 5-1-3-4 shape, leaving him with the sole guard in both black suits. When you cashed the ◊K, followed by the two remaining heart winners, he would be squeezed in spades and clubs.

25. ALAIN LÉVY'S 6NT

France faced Poland in the quarter-finals of the 1997 Bermuda Bowl, contested in Tunisia's Hammamet. Alain Lévy sat South for France on this deal:

```
                    ♠ A 10 9 7 6 5
                    ♡ Q
                    ◇ K Q 3
                    ♣ 10 9 8
      ♠ J 8 4 3                        ♠ Q
      ♡ 7 6 5 4     Both Vul.          ♡ A 10 9 2
      ◇ 9 7 2       Dealer W           ◇ 8 6 4
      ♣ J 3                            ♣ Q 6 5 4 2
                    ♠ K 2
                    ♡ K J 8 3
                    ◇ A J 10 5
                    ♣ A K 7
```

West	North	East	South
Kowalski	*Mari*	*Romanski*	*Lévy*
pass	1♠	pass	2◇
pass	2♠	pass	3♣
pass	3◇	pass	3♡
pass	3♠	pass	4NT
pass	5♠	pass	6NT
all pass			

South's 4NT was Roman Keycard Blackwood, with diamonds agreed, the response showing two keycards and the ◇Q. West led the ♡5, Jacek Romanski winning with the ♡A and returning the ♡2. Lévy won with the ♡K and cashed the ♠K, the ♠Q appearing from East. What is the best continuation for declarer?

The Principle of Restricted Choice states that East's ♠Q is twice as likely to be a singleton as a chosen card from ♠QJ. On this particular deal, however, it is not good enough to consider the spade suit in isolation. If you play a spade to the ace on the second round and find that East started with ♠QJ, you will have six spade tricks and the contract. If instead you follow Restricted Choice and finesse dummy's ♠10 successfully, East showing out, you will have only eleven tricks. Lévy duly played a spade to the ace, going one down when East showed out.

If that were the end of the matter, you would be entitled to turn the page, muttering 'Not much point in that one!' Taking the percentage play in spades, finessing the ♠10, would be right only if the resultant eleven tricks could be converted into twelve subsequently. As you see from the full diagram, this could in fact have been done. East held the sole guard in hearts and clubs. If declarer had cashed four rounds of diamonds and his remaining heart winner before finessing the ♠10, East would have been squeezed when the ♠A was played.

The chance of a simple heart-club squeeze on East was quite small, nowhere near enough to persuade Lévy to abandon the solid chance of dropping the ♠QJ. Look back to Trick 2, now, when Romanski returned the ♡2. Suppose instead that he had returned a much more revealing ♡10, thinking that it could make no difference and would prevent any chance of declarer finessing the ♡8. The slam would surely have been made!

Lévy would have been able to place the ♡9 with East. In that case a twelfth trick would become a certainty after a successful finesse of dummy's ♠10, however the clubs were divided. 'West would hold the spade guard, East would hold the heart guard and neither defender would therefore be able to keep a club guard.' This is the mantra of the double squeeze.

For the sake of illustration, we will swap the minor-suit twos, so that both defenders guard the clubs (West's hand is: ♠J843 ♡7654 ♢97 ♣J32.) The line of play is as for the simple squeeze that we mentioned above. Declarer cashes four rounds of diamonds and these cards remain:

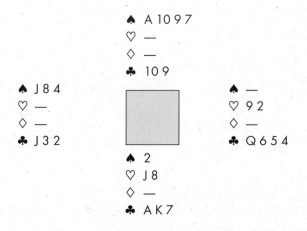

When declarer plays the ♡J, West cannot afford a spade discard or a finesse of the ♠10 will bring in the whole of dummy's suit. He therefore has to throw a club. Declarer now finesses the ♠10 successfully and cashes the ♠A, putting East to two discards. He has to keep the ♡9, to guard against South's ♡8 and therefore has to release two clubs. Declarer scores three tricks with his ♣AK7 and the slam is his.

So, it turns out that there is a lesson to be learnt from the deal. When you are defending, do not play cards that may help declarer to judge which defender holds a guard in a particular suit. Returning the ♡10 would help declarer to place the ♡9. Romanski's actual return of the ♡2 was entirely safe, in practice, since declarer would surely not finesse the ♡8 if he held it.

26. JUSTIN LALL'S FALSECARD AGAINST 6NT

The 2006 World Youth Championships were contested in the exciting location of Bangkok. Justin Lall, for the USA, sat East on this deal played against France:

```
                        ♠ J 7 4
                        ♡ 8 4
                        ◇ A J 9 7 6
                        ♣ K J 7
    ♠ K Q 10 5 3                          ♠ 9 6 2
    ♡ Q 10 7 6        ┌──────────┐        ♡ 9 3
    ◇ Q 8 5           │ Both Vul.│        ◇ 10 4 3
    ♣ 2               │ Dealer E │        ♣ 10 8 6 5 4
                      └──────────┘
                        ♠ A 8
                        ♡ A K J 5 2
                        ◇ K 2
                        ♣ A Q 9 3
```

West	North	East	South
Greenberg	Gaviard	Lall	Bessis
		pass	2♣
pass	2◇	pass	2♡
pass	3◇	pass	3NT
pass	4NT	pass	6♣
pass	6NT	all pass	

Julien Gaviard's 4NT was a limit bid and Thomas Bessis promoted himself to slam. How would you play this when the ♠K is led? There are nine top tricks. If you can find Qxx onside in one of the red suits, the slam will be yours.

Bessis won with the ♠A and cashed two rounds of clubs, discovering that West held a singleton. He then decided to look for gold in the diamond suit. He cashed the ◇K and Justin Lall (East) dropped a deceptive ◇10.

Finessing the ◇J did not look attractive now. Even if the finesse succeeded, it seemed that East would show out and declarer would score only three diamond tricks. Also, the fall of the ◇10 had opened up the possibility that East might hold ◇Q10 doubleton. By rising with the ◇A on the second round, Bessis could give himself two chances. If East had indeed started with ◇Q10, the diamond suit would yield the necessary five tricks. If instead East showed out, or followed with some other diamond, declarer could turn to the heart suit for salvation.

Thomas Bessis played a diamond to the ace, a disappointing ◇3 appearing from East. When a subsequent finesse of the ♡J lost to the queen, the defenders cashed a spade and a diamond for two down. The Americans had bid more accurately at the other table, stopping in game, so Lall's imaginative false card converted a big swing to France into a similar swing to the USA. Well defended!

27. BIDDING 6NT AFTER A PSYCHE

Bidding constructively can be difficult after a psychic opening bid by the opponents. On this deal from the 1986 Lederer Trophy in London, the Journalists faced the Spring Foursomes winners and Gus Calderwood was sitting South.

```
                    ♠ 9 7
                    ♡ K 8 3
                    ◇ Q 6 4 2
                    ♣ K J 10 4
  ♠ K 10 8 4 2                        ♠ 5 3
  ♡ Q 6          ┌─────────┐          ♡ 10 7 5 4 2
  ◇ J 10 9 3     │ Both Vul.│          ◇ 8 7
  ♣ 9 8          │ Dealer W │          ♣ 6 5 3 2
                 └─────────┘
                    ♠ A Q J 6
                    ♡ A J 9
                    ◇ A K 5
                    ♣ A Q 7
```

West	North	East	South
Priday	Breskal	Simpson	Calderwood
pass	pass	1♠	3NT
4♠	4NT	pass	6NT
all pass			

Colin Simpson decided to upgrade his hand and opened with a vulnerable 1♠ in the third seat. Calderwood might have begun with a double but chose instead to bid 3NT. We will never know if North would have advanced over this, because Tony Priday bid 4♠ on the West cards. Calderwood began to sharpen his knife, only to see partner raise to 4NT. Deprived of a penalty that would have taken some time to calculate, he then had to make twelve tricks in 6NT. How would you tackle this task when West leads the ◇J?

Calderwood won the ◇J lead in his hand and crossed to dummy with a club to finesse the ♠Q. When the finesse failed, he had only eleven top tricks. The diamonds were unlikely to break 3-3, after the opening lead, but various squeeze chances were present. West was marked with the spade length; if he held a diamond guard, as was likely after the opening lead, he could be squeezed in spades and diamonds. Declarer's next move was to cash the ♡A and ♡K, since it would also be possible to squeeze East if he held the guards in both red suits. This preparatory move brought an unexpected reward when the ♡Q fell doubleton from West, giving declarer his slam.

Does lightning ever strike twice? It does in the Lederer Trophy! A mere seventeen years later, the VuGraph coverage of the last round of the 2003 event featured David Burn and Zia Mahmood facing the wily Canadians, Joey Silver and John Carruthers. There was an entertaining firework display on this board:

```
                    ♠ 9 8 5
                    ♡ A 9 7 3
                    ◇ Q J 10 9 7 4
                    ♣ —
  ♠ 3 2                              ♠ A 10 7 4
  ♡ J 10 8 6 5    Neither Vul.      ♡ 4 2
  ◇ 8 3 2         Dealer W           ◇ 6 5
  ♣ 9 5 3                            ♣ A 10 8 6 4
                    ♠ K Q J 6
                    ♡ K Q
                    ◇ A K
                    ♣ K Q J 7 2
```

West	North	East	South
Silver	Zia	Carruthers	Burn
1♡	pass	1NT	dbl
2♣	2♡	2♠	dbl
pass	4◇	pass	4NT
pass	6◇	pass	6NT
pass	pass	dbl	all pass

Silver psyched 1♡ and his partner responded with a forcing 1NT. Burn doubled and Silver made a further psychic bid, showing his second 'suit'. Zia indicated good values with a heart cuebid and Carruthers showed excellent club support, with the artificial bid of 2♠.

The bidding climbed ever upwards until Zia reached 6◇, which had excellent chances thanks to North's club void. The contract was then amended to 6NT by David Burn, who in a later report amusingly described this as 'the bid of a man bewildered by the whole affair'. East could not be denied his two aces and the slam was one down, doubled.

The board produced some attractive play at another table. Georges Iontzeff, sitting South for France, ended in 6◇ played from the short trump holding. How would you have tackled this contract when West leads the ♡J?

With the favorable breaks, it is possible to arrange a heart ruff. Iontzeff followed a different path. He won the heart lead in his hand and drew two rounds of trumps. He then reached dummy with a club ruff and drew West's last trump. When declarer led a spade towards his hand, East ducked and South won with the king. A club ruff to dummy was followed by a second spade; East ducked again and declarer won with the queen. These cards remained:

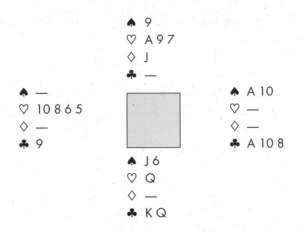

                    ♠ 9
                    ♡ A 9 7
                    ◇ J
                    ♣ —
♠ —   ♠ A 10
♡ 10 8 6 5   ♡ —
◇ —   ◇ —
♣ 9   ♣ A 10 8
                    ♠ J 6
                    ♡ Q
                    ◇ —
                    ♣ K Q

Iontzeff now made the loser-on-loser play of the ♣K, discarding dummy's last spade. Poor East had no safe return. If he played the ♠A, declarer would ruff in the dummy and cross to his hand with the ♡Q. The slam would then be made without scoring the ♡A. If instead East returned a club, declarer would win with the ♣Q, cash the ♡Q and cross to dummy with a spade ruff to enjoy the ♡A.

Quiz 16 *How would you play 6NT?*

                    ♠ A K Q J 3
                    ♡ A Q J 6
                    ◇ A 4
                    ♣ 9 7
♣Q led
                    ♠ 10 6 2
                    ♡ 8 7 5 3
                    ◇ K J 7 2
                    ♣ A K

West	North	East	South
3♣	dbl	pass	3NT
pass	6NT	all pass	

West leads the ♣Q against 6NT. All will be easy if hearts break 3-2, but perhaps West holds a singleton heart. How will you play the contract? **(The answer is overleaf.)**

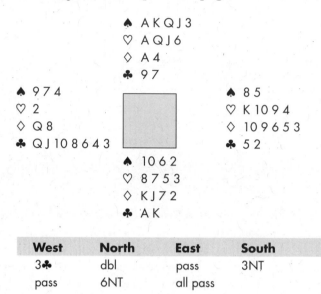

West	North	East	South
3♣	dbl	pass	3NT
pass	6NT	all pass	

You win the ♣Q lead and finesse the ♡Q. East takes the ♡K and returns the ♡10, West discarding a club. You have eleven top tricks and the diamond finesse for a twelfth trick. By cashing your black-suit winners, however, you can put East under pressure and thereby create an extra chance. After winning East's heart return, you cash your winners outside diamonds, reaching this end position:

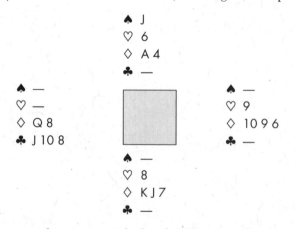

You have a complete count on the hand. When you play the ♠J, East has to throw another diamond to retain his heart guard. The defenders' remaining diamonds are known to be 2-2 and there is no temptation to take the diamond finesse. When you play the ◇A and ◇K instead, the ◇Q falls from West and you make the slam.

You would have made the contract even if your ◇J had instead been the ◇3. With the ◇J in your hand, the technique is classified as a 'show-up squeeze'. When East's last diamond 'shows up', you know that West holds the ◇Q.

28. MIKE MOSS'S 6NT

The final of the 1990 Rosenblum Cup (the World Knockout championship) saw teams from Germany and the USA in opposition. Mike Moss sat South for the Americans on this deal:

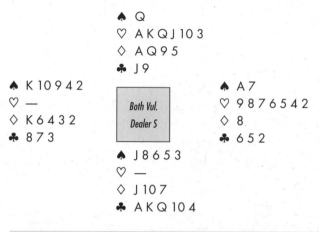

West	North	East	South
Rohowsky	Coon	Nippgen	Moss
			1♣
2♠	3♡	pass	3NT
pass	6NT	all pass	

So, in a world final, Mike Moss found himself in 6NT with the ace and king of spades missing. Also, the defender on lead had made a vulnerable 2♠ overcall!

Roland Rohowsky had no reason to lead a spade from his actual holding. With the opponents in 6NT, the odds were high that they held the ace and queen of spades between them. He placed the ◊3 on the table and Moss could now count twelve likely tricks: six heart tricks, unless they broke 6-1 or 7-0, five club tricks and the ◊A. 'Ace, please,' he said.

When declarer played dummy's other red ace he was stunned to see West show out. There was no way to recover and the slam went one down. When the board was replayed, the German North-South pair picked up +720 for their unadventurous 3NT+4. So, Moss's failure to finesse in diamonds at Trick 1 had changed a 13 IMP swing to the USA into a 13 IMP swing to Germany. By a cruel coincidence, 13 IMPs proved to be Germany's eventual winning margin.

The commentators at the time pointed out that West's spades could be at best ♠A109xxx after his failure to lead the suit; West was therefore likely to hold the ◊K for his vulnerable overcall. Oh yes? As I see it, only a madman would have finessed in diamonds.

29. KIT WOOLSEY'S 6NT

The USA's Grand National Teams championship is a battle between the champion teams of each district of the ACBL. It was first held in 1975 and the winning team has nearly always contained at least one world champion. Jeff Meckstroth has won the event seven times. We will take a look at a 6NT contract from the 2003 Grand National Teams. It was played by Kit Woolsey.

```
                    ♠ K Q 6
                    ♡ A
                    ♢ Q J 10 6 5 4
                    ♣ 7 6 5
   ♠ 9 8                              ♠ J 10 7 3 2
   ♡ J 9 7 2        Both Vul.        ♡ 10 8
   ♢ 9 8 7 3 2      Dealer N         ♢ A
   ♣ 9 4                              ♣ Q 10 8 3 2
                    ♠ A 5 4
                    ♡ K Q 6 5 4 3
                    ♢ K
                    ♣ A K J
```

West	North	East	South
			Woolsey
	1♢	pass	1♡
pass	2♢	pass	4NT
pass	5♢	pass	6NT
all pass			

West led the ♢9 to East's ace. Woolsey won the club return with the ace and crossed to the ♡A to test the diamonds. When he played dummy's ♢Q, East discarded a spade. How would you attempt to recover from this body blow?

Woolsey returned to his hand with the ♠A to try his luck in the other red suit. All followed to the ♡K but East discarded a club on the ♡Q. Declarer had eleven tricks on top and the only obvious chance of a twelfth was to finesse the ♣J. West was known to guard both the red suits, but a red-suit squeeze was impossible because there was no communication in either suit. If West happened to hold the ♣Q in addition to his two red-suit guards, however, he would be unable to defend the position.

Woolsey returned to dummy with a spade and cashed two more top diamonds. He had reached this end position:

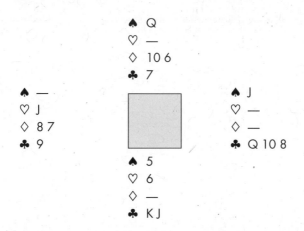

```
              ♠ Q
              ♡ —
              ◇ 10 6
              ♣ 7
♠ —                        ♠ J
♡ J                        ♡ —
◇ 8 7                      ◇ —
♣ 9                        ♣ Q 10 8
              ♠ 5
              ♡ 6
              ◇ —
              ♣ K J
```

When Woolsey played dummy's ♠Q, West had to retain the ♡J and both his diamonds. He therefore had to throw his last club. If this had been the queen, South's ♣J would have become good for a twelfth trick. Woolsey cashed the ◇10, throwing the ♡6 and then led a club towards his hand. West's last two cards were known to be the ♡J and the ◇8, so he was able to finesse the ♣J with complete certainty.

Since the ♣Q was onside all along, you may think that it is a deal for the purist. Perhaps you're right. It's rather pretty, though, don't you think?

Quiz 17 *How would you play 6NT?*

```
              ♠ K J 4 3
              ♡ A 8
              ◇ K Q 7 6 5
              ♣ 5 4
♣10 led       [               ]
              ♠ A Q 10
              ♡ Q J 3 2
              ◇ A 9 4 2
              ♣ A K
```

West	North	East	South
			2NT
pass	6NT	all pass	

You win the ♣10 lead and play a diamond to the king, East discarding a club. What now? **(The answer is overleaf.)**

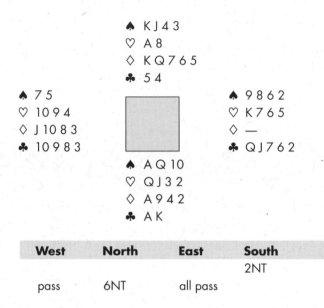

West	North	East	South
			2NT
pass	6NT	all pass	

With adequate values for 6NT, North wisely decides not to look for a diamond or spade fit. West leads the ♣10, won with the ace, and a diamond to the king reveals the 4-0 break. How will you attempt to recover the situation?

There are ten top tricks. If West holds the ♡K, you can simply run the heart queen. With the total then up to eleven tricks, you could afford to concede a diamond trick, establishing your twelfth trick from that source. How likely is it that West will hold the ♡K, though? West holds four diamonds to East's none, so the Law of Vacant Spaces suggests that East is more likely than his partner to hold the ♡K. Indeed, you can see from the diagram that East is longer than West in all three suits outside diamonds. He is therefore the favorite to hold any particular missing card in one of those suits. Can you make the slam when East holds the ♡K?

When the bad diamond break comes to light, you should continue with four rounds of spades (you can afford this because you still have adequate entries in the minor suits). This gives you some further distributional information. West began with six cards in spades and diamonds to East's four. So, East is still the favorite to hold the ♡K. You continue by leading the ♡8 towards your hand. East is caught in a Morton's Fork position. If he rises with the king he will give you a total of three heart tricks, enough for the contract. Let's assume that he senses this and plays low instead, the ♡Q winning. You then jump on your camel and head towards the other well — the diamond suit. You concede a diamond trick to West and will have twelve tricks. This last move would not be possible, of course, if you had played ace and another heart instead, releasing your control of the heart suit.

30. INTO AND OUT OF 6NT

The time has come for us to enjoy an exciting board from the Cap Gemini 13th World Top tournament in 1999. One pair was doubled in six of a suit and rescued themselves into 6NT. At another table a pair was doubled in 6NT on the very same board and rescued themselves into seven of a suit! This was the auction at the first table, where Peter Jansen and Jan Westerhof of the Netherlands faced the Austrians, Doris Fischer and Terry Weigkricht:

```
              ♠ 4
              ♡ A 4
              ◇ A Q J 9 4 3 2
              ♣ 6 5 4
♠ 7                              ♠ 8 6 5 2
♡ K Q 10 8 7 6 5   Neither Vul.  ♡ 9 3 2
◇ 8 7              Dealer E       ◇ 10
♣ Q J 2                          ♣ A K 10 8 7
              ♠ A K Q J 10 9 3
              ♡ J
              ◇ K 6 5
              ♣ 9 3
```

West	North	East	South
Jansen	Fischer	Westerhof	Weigkricht
		pass	1♠
3♡	4◇	4♡	4NT
pass	5♡	pass	6♠
pass	pass	dbl	pass
pass	6NT	dbl	all pass

Gambling on the club position, Weigkricht opted for Blackwood at her second turn. She was soon in 6♠ and this was doubled by Westerhof in the pass-out seat. What did this double mean, would you say?

Since the slam had been freely bid, it was clearly a lead-directing double. West would know for certain that partner did not want a heart lead, but did he want a diamond or a club? Most often, a Lightner Double suggests a void (or occasionally the ace-king or ace-queen) in dummy's first bid suit. Fearing a diamond void with East, Fischer corrected the contract to 6NT. Westerhof doubled again and it was now up to Jansen to decide what this pair of doubles had meant.

A diamond void, the most likely reason for a double of 6♠, would be no asset when defending 6NT. South's immediate Blackwood bid also perhaps suggested a fitting diamond honor, allowing her to visualize a slam on two running suits. Well, we can all see that a club lead would have given the defenders the first five tricks. This was not at all obvious to poor Peter Jansen and who can blame him for leading a top heart honor, allowing the doubled slam to be made with an overtrick?

If you think 6NT was rather too high a final resting spot on those cards, wait until you see what happened at another table:

West	North	East	South
Lévy	Zia	Chemla	Forrester
		pass	1♠
3♡	3NT	4♡	4NT
pass	6◇	pass	6NT
pass	pass	dbl	7♠
all pass			

Paul Chemla found himself on lead against 6NT with an ace-king in his hand. How many players can put their hand on their heart and say that they would not have doubled in such a situation? Not Chemla, anyway! He doubled 6NT and Tony Forrester was quick to diagnose the situation and adjust the contract to 7♠. Unlike at the other table, this change of contract put a different defender on lead.

We must now express sympathy for Alain Lévy. He had to unravel the auction and assess the meaning (if any) of the lack of a final double across the table. He chose to lead a heart honor, as Jensen had done at the other table. Forrester was then able to face his cards, claiming the doubled grand slam.

Quiz 18 *How would you play 6NT?*

```
                    ♠ A 8 5
                    ♡ 8 7 5 4
                    ◇ J 7 6 4
                    ♣ 7 5
   ♣J led           ▭▭▭▭▭
                    ♠ K J 7
                    ♡ A K Q
                    ◇ A K
                    ♣ A K Q 6 4
```

West	North	East	South
			2♣
pass	2◇	3♠	4NT
pass	6NT	all pass	

West leads the ♣J, East discarding a spade. How will you play the contract? (**The answer is on page 89.**)

31. ANDREW ROBSON'S 6NT

In the 1993 Cap Gemini World Top tournament, Andrew Robson and Tony Forrester finished in second place behind the Brazilians, Gabriel Chagas and Marcelo Branco. Robson sat South on this remarkable deal:

```
                    ♠ A Q 8
                    ♡ A 10 5
                    ◇ K 9 7 5
                    ♣ A K 6
    ♠ 7 6 4                          ♠ 10 9 3 2
    ♡ Q J 7 4      Neither Vul.      ♡ 9 8 3
    ◇ J 6 3        Dealer S          ◇ Q 2
    ♣ 9 4 2                          ♣ J 10 8 7
                    ♠ K J 5
                    ♡ K 6 2
                    ◇ A 10 8 4
                    ♣ Q 5 3
```

West	North	East	South
Westra	Forrester	Leufkens	Robson
			1NT
pass	4NT	pass	6NT
all pass			

Robson opened with a 12-14 1NT and no one can accuse Tony Forrester of overbidding when he made the non-forcing limit bid of 4NT on his 20-count. Robson accepted the try on his mid-range hand, hoping that the ◇10 would have a role to play. Put the two hands together and you have a truly awful 6NT contract. It is a reminder to us all, how impotent hands with a 4-3-3-3 shape can be.

West led the ♠6 and it seemed at first that declarer would need four diamond tricks to land the slam. This could be done if one defender held a singleton honor, provided declarer guessed to play the right top card first. Robson won the spade lead and chose to cash the ◇A, no interesting card showing. How would you have continued the play?

Robson saw that there was a remote chance of an endplay. He cashed his remaining black-suit winners and exited with king and another diamond. Enri Leufkens won the third round of diamonds in the West seat and, to declarer's good fortune, had no black-suit winner to cash. West was on lead in this end position:

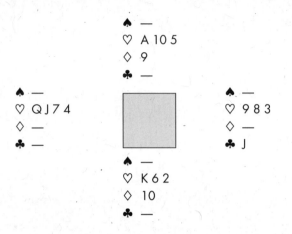

```
              ♠ —
              ♡ A 10 5
              ◇ 9
              ♣ —
♠ —                          ♠ —
♡ Q J 7 4    ┌──────────┐    ♡ 9 8 3
◇ —          │          │    ◇ —
♣ —          └──────────┘    ♣ J
              ♠ —
              ♡ K 6 2
              ◇ 10
              ♣ —
```

Leufkens exited with the ♡4 and Robson called for dummy's ♡10. When this won the trick, he muttered his thanks to the Bridge Gods and claimed the slam.

I was rather surprised that West chose to exit with a low heart. This would make life very easy for declarer if he held ♡K92, whereas exiting with an honor would give him a guess.

You may think that West played for declarer to hold ♡K82, in which case he might run the low card to his hand, hoping that West held ♡Q9xx or ♡ J9xx. That could hardly be the case at this level; with either of those holdings, West would have given declarer no chance by exiting with the honor card.

Quiz 19 *How would you play 6NT?*

```
              ♠ Q J
              ♡ K Q 2
              ◇ J 10 8 7
              ♣ A Q 5 3
◇9 led        ┌──────────┐
              └──────────┘
              ♠ A 8 7 5 3
              ♡ A 9 5
              ◇ A K
              ♣ K J 9
```

West	North	East	South
	1◇	pass	2♠
pass	3♠	pass	3NT
pass	6NT	all pass	

West leads the ◇9 and you play dummy's ◇J. This fails to flush out East's ◇Q, to no-one's great surprise, and you win in the South hand. How will you continue? **(The answer is on page 92.)**

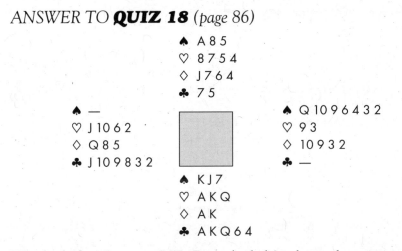

West leads the ♣J against 6NT. East, who bid 3♠ during the auction, discards a spade. You have ten top tricks. If hearts break 3-3, you can score an extra trick in the suit and take the marked spade finesse for the contract. What if hearts do not break 3-3? The spade finesse would give you an eleventh trick but there would be no chance whatsoever of a twelfth trick.

If West turns up with four hearts, your best chance is to find him with the ◇Q as well. You can then catch him in a repeating squeeze. You win the club lead and play the three top hearts, East showing out on the third round. The spade finesse is no use to you now. To set up a squeeze against West, you will need to rectify the count by losing a spade trick to East! You therefore lead the ♠J and run it to East's ♠Q. You win the spade return in your hand and cash the ◇AK. These cards remain:

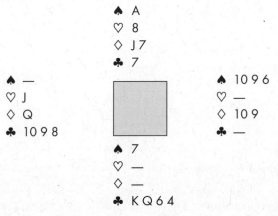

When you lead the ♠7, West cannot throw another club or you will score four club tricks for the contract. If he throws a red-suit guard, you will win with dummy's ♠A and cash the established red-suit winner. This will squeeze West again, forcing him to abandon his guard in either clubs or the other red suit.

It was a fiendishly difficult problem, you're right. Sorry about that!

32. MEADOWLARK'S 6NT

My wife, Thelma, is hooked on the Meadowlark bridge computer program, which allows you to bid and play the South hand while computer characters bid and play the other three hands.

'Move aside,' I said to her the other evening. 'Let me have a go.'

Somewhat reluctantly, she allowed me to take control of the keyboard. For the moment, we could see only the South hand shown below. Following my wife's preferred methods, which had been specified to Meadowlark, I opened a 12-14 point 1NT. This was raised to 4NT by the computer player sitting North. Knowing that I would be playing the contract, I raised confidently to 6NT.

West led the ♣7 and the dummy's cards appeared on the screen. This was the layout:

```
                    ♠ A 8 6
                    ♡ A K 9
                    ◇ A Q 9 3
                    ♣ Q 6 3
  ♠ 9 7                              ♠ J 10 5 2
  ♡ 7 4 3          Both Vul.         ♡ Q 6 5
  ◇ 8 6 5 4 2      Dealer S          ◇ J 10
  ♣ 7 5 4                            ♣ K J 10 8
                    ♠ K Q 4 3
                    ♡ J 10 8 2
                    ◇ K 7
                    ♣ A 9 2
```

West	North	East	South
Computer	*Computer*	*Computer*	*DB*
			1NT
pass	4NT	pass	6NT
all pass			

Dummy had only 19 points and 4-3-3-3 shape. The program had no doubt bid aggressively, sensing that a masterful declarer had just taken charge.

'A human player wouldn't lead from a king against 6NT,' I explained to my wife, 'but the computer may have done.' I played the ♣Q from dummy; East produced the ♣K and I won with the ♣A.

'The computer is probably silly enough to cover the ♡J with the ♡Q,' I continued. 'If West doesn't cover, I'm going to play to drop the queen from East.' The ♡J was not covered, so I tried the ace and king from dummy, failing to drop the queen.

In desperation I cleared a heart trick. East won with the ♡Q and mercilessly cashed three clubs. I was down three, vulnerable, and Thelma seemed unappreciative of my efforts.

An attractive feature of the Meadowlark program is that you can ask for all the deals in a session to be pre-played by various computer characters (different types of birds, such as Pelicans, Vultures and Swallows). Thelma displayed the other scores for the present deal. 'The Eagles made 6NT,' she said, accusingly.

'Impossible!' I replied.

We inspected the play record from the table where 6NT had been made. Once again the ♣7 had been led, but the Eagle sitting South played low from dummy and allowed East's ♣10 to win. The computer East (a Booby, appropriately) returned the ♣K to the ♣A.

'Absurd defense,' I muttered.

The Eagle declarer cashed four rounds of diamonds, having noted (with an eagle-eye) the fall of East's ◊J10. When he continued with the ♣Q, which had been so helpfully established by the defenders, East was squeezed in the major suits. A twelfth trick resulted and that was plus 1440 instead of my minus 300.

'Do you see where you went wrong?' Thelma asked.

```
                    ♠ Q J
                    ♡ K Q 2
                    ◊ J 10 8 7
                    ♣ A Q 5 3
    ♠ 9 6 4 2                        ♠ K 10
    ♡ J 6 4 3                        ♡ 10 8 7
    ◊ 9 3                            ◊ Q 6 5 4 2
    ♣ 10 4 2                         ♣ 8 7 6
                    ♠ A 8 7 5 3
                    ♡ A 9 5
                    ◊ A K
                    ♣ K J 9
```

West	North	East	South
	1◊	pass	2♠
pass	3♠	pass	3NT
pass	6NT	all pass	

The deal comes from a match between Argentina and the USA. As the bidding suggests, it was many years ago now! West leads the ◊9 against 6NT and you cover with dummy's ◊J, hoping that East is half asleep and will surrender his queen. No, he plays low and you win with the ◊K. How will you continue?

The American declarer played a low spade to dummy's queen. East won with the king and returned the ♠10. When the spades failed to break 3-3, the slam was one down.

It was not a very distinguished line of play. A much better idea is to cross to a heart at Trick 2 and to run the ♠Q from dummy. Whether or not East covers, you will have nine tricks outside diamonds and can simply surrender a trick to East's ◊Q to carry you past the finishing line.

What if West wins when you run the ♠Q? You will then need a 3-3 spade break. A spade-diamond squeeze is unlikely to materialize, because West could break it up by returning a second round of spades.

I can sense that you would very much like to know what happened at the other table of the USA-Argentina match. All right, I'll tell you. North opened 1♣, instead of 1◊, and ended in 6♣. All thirteen tricks were made, in this rather unlikely contract, thanks to the friendly lie of the black suits. Trumps were drawn in three rounds and the ♠Q was covered by the king and ace. When the ♠10 fell under North's ♠J, South's ♠87 were good for a ruffing finesse against West's ♠9!

PART TWO
6NT - Fiction

33. THE HEADMASTER'S POOR DISCARD

'That last board was truly awful,' exclaimed the Headmaster, as the opponents made their way from the table. 'Surely you knew there was still a trump out?'

'To tell the truth, I was more concerned about the diamonds,' the Reverend Benson replied. 'Mind you, I don't think we should have been in game. You didn't have a particularly good fit for my game-try suit.'

With some difficulty the Headmaster managed to restrain himself. 'Draw the last trump and you make it easily,' he said.

Two fourth formers, John Hutson and Neil Phillips, took their seats at the table. 'Are you having a good session, Headmaster?' Hutson asked.

The Headmaster made no reply, reaching for his cards. If anyone else asked that question, he would scream. Even a world champion would finish below average with Benson as a partner. This was the first deal of the round:

```
                  ♠ A K 10 7
                  ♡ J 10 4
                  ◇ 5 4 2
                  ♣ A Q 6
  ♠ J 9 5 4 2                      ♠ 6
  ♡ —            ┌──────────┐      ♡ K Q 9 8 6 3 2
  ◇ J 8 6        │ Both Vul.│      ◇ Q 10 9 3
  ♣ J 9 8 4 3    │ Dealer E │      ♣ 7
                 └──────────┘
                  ♠ Q 8 3
                  ♡ A 7 5
                  ◇ A K 7
                  ♣ K 10 5 2
```

West	North	East	South
Reverend	Neil	Head-	John
Benson	Phillips	master	Hutson
		3♡	3NT
pass	4NT	pass	5♡
pass	6NT	all pass	

The Reverend Benson had read somewhere that it was the mark of a poor player to lead from a jack. Was it his fault that he had picked up such a hand? His lead was bound to cost a trick and the Headmaster would shout at him again. Ah well, the clubs were strongest. He had better try one of them.

The Headmaster turned toward the South player. 'What was the meaning of your partner's 4NT?' he demanded.

'It was Blackwood, Sir,' John Hutson replied.

Neil Phillips looked alarmed. 'I didn't intend it as Blackwood,' he said. 'I wanted you to go on if you were maximum.'

'Oh dear, I'm completely minimum,' Hutson replied. 'Sorry, partner.'

When the young declarer won the first trick with the ♣10, the Headmaster glared across the table. Had Benson led from the jack? It would be typical of him to let these young lads off the hook after their ridiculous bidding misunderstanding.

When the ace and queen of spades were played, the Headmaster showed out on the second round. Hutson took the marked finesse of dummy's ♠10 and cashed the ♠K. The ace and queen of clubs were followed by a diamond to the ace, leaving these cards still to be played:

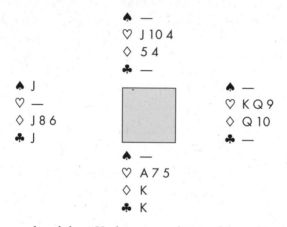

    ♠ —
    ♡ J 10 4
    ◇ 5 4
    ♣ —

♠ J   ♠ —
♡ —   ♡ K Q 9
◇ J 8 6   ◇ Q 10
♣ J   ♣ —

    ♠ —
    ♡ A 7 5
    ◇ K
    ♣ K

John Hutson played the ♣K, throwing a diamond from dummy. The Headmaster, sitting East, did not like the look of this. If he threw a heart, declarer would surely be able to play ace and another heart, setting up a twelfth trick in that suit. It seemed that he would have to throw a diamond instead, relying on Benson to provide some assistance in the suit.

The diamond discard brought the Headmaster little joy. Hutson played the ◇K, removing East's last card in the suit, and continued with a heart to the jack. The Headmaster had to win with one honor and lead away from the other. The slam had been made.

The Reverend Benson smiled to himself. 'I'm surprised you didn't see that endplay coming, Headmaster,' he observed.

Against all the odds the Headmaster held back a suitable expletive. 'There was nothing I could do about it,' he replied. 'Your foolish lead, away from a jack, handed it to them on a plate.'

Looking somewhat disgruntled, the Reverend Benson sat back in his chair. The Headmaster was becoming a parody of himself. He makes the wrong discard, walks into an obvious endplay, and then tries to blame it all on his partner! Still, it would hardly be appropriate to expose his superior's shortcomings in front of two boys. 'Sorry, Headmaster,' he said.

34. SERGEANT BARKER'S ABERRATION

The Abbot's ancient Morris Minor pulled up at the red and white barrier outside the Worthy Down army camp. An armed sentry approached and peered suspiciously at the four occupants of the car. 'May I ask your business here, Sir?'

The Abbot summoned his patience. 'We're here to play a bridge match,' he replied.

The sentry consulted his clipboard. 'There are two matches down here,' he said. 'Are you Abbot Hugo Yorke-Smith or er... Dr Rapanjibat Singh?'

'Take a wild guess,' replied the Abbot. 'Come on, let us through. We're twenty minutes late already.'

The local league match was soon underway in the brightly lit officers' mess. This was an early board at the Abbot's table:

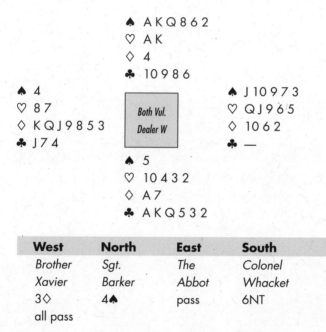

West	North	East	South
Brother	Sgt.	The	Colonel
Xavier	Barker	Abbot	Whacket
3◇	4♠	pass	6NT
all pass			

Brother Xavier led the ◇K and the splendidly mustached Colonel Whacket won with the ace. When he played the ♣A, East discarded a heart. 'No need to worry, Sergeant,' he said. 'My clubs are all good, anyway.'

A small flaw in this analysis became apparent when the Colonel cashed the ♣K and ♣Q and only then noticed that dummy's ♣10 was blocking the suit. Annoying, what? Still, maybe the spades would break. The spade suit failed to rescue him and he was soon two down.

'Damned bad luck in the club suit!' the Colonel exclaimed. 'If the jack falls in two rounds, I can cross to the ten and come back to the queen.'

'That's right, Sir,' his partner replied. 'Maybe you should duck the diamond lead, Sir? Then you can throw one of dummy's clubs on the ace, Sir.'

The Colonel rose angrily to his feet. 'Sergeant Barker!'

'Sir!'

'It's against mess rules to criticize the play of an officer. If it happens again, you'll be on a charge. Understood?'

'Sir!'

Brother Xavier raised an eyebrow at this exchange. For years he had assumed that the Abbot was the worst partner in the world. Perhaps he had been wrong.

The Abbot was determined to make the most of the situation. 'I doubt it will matter very much,' he informed the Colonel. 'Our teammates are very forward bidders; they're hardly likely to miss the grand slam in clubs on those values.'

A few boards later, Sergeant Barker picked up one of the finest hands he had ever held. Rather unexpectedly it was his partner, Colonel Whacket, who opened the bidding.

```
              ♠ A K Q 10 6 2
              ♡ A K J 6
              ◇ A K 4
              ♣ —
♠ 9 4 3                        ♠ J 7
♡ 7 2          NS Vul.          ♡ Q 9 8 5 3
◇ 10 7 6       Dealer S         ◇ Q 9 3
♣ 9 7 5 3 2                     ♣ 8 6 4
              ♠ 8 5
              ♡ 10 4
              ◇ J 8 5 2
              ♣ A K Q J 10
```

West	North	East	South
Brother	Sgt.	The	Colonel
Xavier	Barker	Abbot	Whacket
			1♣
pass	2♠	pass	3♣
pass	3♡	pass	3NT
pass	4◇	pass	4NT
pass	6NT	all pass	

Sergeant Barker bid 6NT, rather than 6♠, in case there was a hostile spade break. The ♠9 was led and Sgt. Barker laid out the dummy in three immaculately straight lines, as if it were some well-polished kit awaiting inspection.

'A splendid dummy, Sergeant,' declared the Colonel. Mind you, he thought, how the Devil can I reach my hand to score all the clubs? Thirty years as a commanding officer did bring some rewards and he soon had his plan of campaign ready. He would cover the ♠9 with the ♠10! East could win a cheap trick with the ♠J, yes, but the ♠8 would then be established as an entry to his hand. Brilliant! 'Play the ten,' he said.

The Abbot eyed this card suspiciously. Realizing what declarer was up to, he allowed dummy's ♠10 to win the trick.

Somewhat annoyed that the enemy had countered his first attack, the Colonel continued with dummy's ♡J. If the defenders captured this card, the ♡10 would become an entry to his hand. With the air of a multiple world champion in his prime, the Abbot held back his ♡Q, following with a low card.

Colonel Whacket cashed his major-suit winners, arriving at this end position:

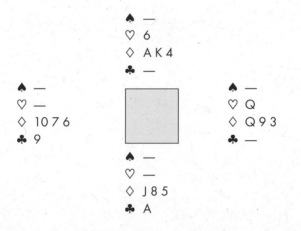

East would not have released a winning heart just to hold on to a small club, so each defender must have exactly three diamonds. Now, who held the ◇Q? If it was East, a heart exit would endplay him. If it was West, three rounds of diamonds would force him to play a club to the stranded ace in the South hand. The vital queen seemed to have left no clue as to her whereabouts. The Colonel, a great believer in Fate, decided to make a random choice.

'When is your wife's birthday, Sergeant?' he asked suddenly. If it was an odd day of the month, he would play East for the ◇Q.

'Some time in March, Sir,' replied Sergeant Barker. He had been trained to obey officers' commands without question, however stupid they seemed.

'Yes, yes, but what day of the month?' persisted the Colonel.

'I think it's the 16th, Sir.'

'Right, play the ace of diamonds,' continued the Colonel confidently. 'Yes, and the king of diamonds… and a small diamond.'

When this proved to be the wrong decision and the slam went down, the Colonel swept up his cards angrily and thrust them back in the wallet.

'Or is it the 15th?' said Sergeant Barker thoughtfully. 'Yes, I rather think it is. I'll ask her when I get home, Sir, and draft a report for you in the morning!'

35. THE MOTHER SUPERIOR'S CLUE

'Goodness me, it's been cold today,' declared the Mother of Discipline as she lowered herself into her seat. 'The Good Lord no doubt sees a purpose in this freezing weather but it escapes me at the moment.'

The Mother Superior smiled serenely. 'Every day is a chance to do good work and help others,' she replied. 'I hardly notice the temperature, myself.'

'You will when you get to my age,' continued the Mother of Discipline. 'It's absurd that we have no fire in the cardroom. It'll be November next week.'

The players drew their cards for this deal:

```
                    ♠ J 7 5
                    ♡ K 10 9 3
                    ◇ A K 5
                    ♣ Q 9 6
    ♠ A 10 9 3 2                      ♠ 8 4
    ♡ Q 8 5         Neither Vul.      ♡ 7 6 2
    ◇ J 2           Dealer S          ◇ 10 9 7 6 4
    ♣ 8 7 5                           ♣ 10 3 2
                    ♠ K Q 6
                    ♡ A J 4
                    ◇ Q 8 3
                    ♣ A K J 4
```

West	North	East	South
Mother of	Sister	Sister	Mother
Discipline	Grace	Thomas	Superior
			2NT
pass	6NT	all pass	

The Mother of Discipline led the ♣8, following her usual practice of choosing a safe lead against 6NT. Dummy went down and the Mother Superior noted that she would have eleven top tricks once the ♠A was dislodged. To score a twelfth trick, she would then have to guess which defender held the ♡Q. She nodded thoughtfully. It was basic technique to play the other three side suits first. The defender with the majority of the hearts would then be favorite to hold the ♡Q.

The Mother Superior won the first trick with dummy's ♣Q and led a spade to the king. With 20 points on view in her own hand and the dummy, the Mother of Discipline knew that declarer must hold all the missing honors. She won with the ♠A and returned a second round of clubs.

The Mother Superior played off her remaining winners in spades, diamonds and clubs, but the outcome of all this detective work was disappointing. If East had begun with, say, four hearts to West's two, she would have been twice as likely as West to hold the heart queen. Unfortunately East and West had begun with three hearts each!

The Mother Superior led the ♡J from her hand. The Mother of Discipline, as was obvious from her appearance, had not been born yesterday. She followed smoothly with a low card, hoping that declarer would misguess.

'Play low, will you,' said the Mother Superior. East followed impotently with a low card and the slam had been made.

The Mother of Discipline was less than pleased that a slam had been made against her. 'Lucky guess in hearts, Reverend Mother,' she said. 'No particular reason to play me for the queen, was there?'

'I usually play for the queen to lie over the jack,' replied the Mother Superior. 'It's right as often as it's wrong, I find.'

The second board of the round was played in an unexceptional partscore and the change of round was called. Sucking in air between her teeth, the ancient Mother of Discipline struggled to her feet and headed for another table.

Sister Grace shared a smile with the Mother Superior. 'Queen lying over the jack?' she said. 'You were pulling her leg, weren't you?'

'Of course,' replied the Mother Superior. 'I've a lot of respect for the old dear, as you know, but her complaints about the weather get on my nerves.'

'Restricted Choice, wasn't it?' continued Sister Grace.

'Yes, yes,' said the Mother Superior, chuckling to herself. 'If the Mother of Discipline held three small hearts, she might well have led a heart instead of club. Even though hearts were 3-3, the fact that she chose to lead a club made her a two-to-one favorite to hold the queen of hearts!'

Quiz 20 How would you play 6NT?

```
            ♠ A 5
            ♡ Q 7 5 2
            ◇ A J 7 2
            ♣ K J 3
♡J led      ▭▭▭▭▭
            ♠ K 8 7 4
            ♡ A K 6 3
            ◇ K 6
            ♣ A Q 4
```

West	North	East	South
		3♠	3NT
pass	6NT	all pass	

West leads the ♡J, East following with the ♡4. Hearts are likely to break 4-1. How will you tackle the slam? **(The answer is on page 104.)**

36. BROTHER AELRED'S UNUSUAL SQUEEZE

Most of the St. Titus monks would not dream of competing at the monastery £1 table. It would be an expensive affair, playing the way they did, and they felt more at home on the 5p table.

'It's you and me, then,' said the ancient Brother Sextus, trying to look pleased that he had cut Brother Aelred as partner. Ah well, it wouldn't cost too much at these stakes.

This was the first deal of the rubber:

```
                    ♠ A K J 7 6
                    ♡ 5
                    ◇ 8 4 3
                    ♣ A K 6 2
    ♠ —                              ♠ Q 10 9 8 4 3
    ♡ J 9 7 3        Neither Vul.    ♡ 10 8 6 2
    ◇ Q 10 9 7 6 5                   ◇ —
    ♣ 10 9 8         Dealer N        ♣ 7 5 3
                    ♠ 5 2
                    ♡ A K Q 4
                    ◇ A K J 2
                    ♣ Q J 4
```

West	North	East	South
Brother	Brother	Brother	Brother
Michael	Sextus	Zac	Aelred
	1♠	pass	4NT
pass	5♡	pass	6NT
all pass			

An unimpressive rubber bridge auction, involving simple Blackwood, carried Brother Aelred to 6NT. Since he rarely managed to score as many as twelve tricks, let alone thirteen, he made no attempt to investigate a grand slam. The ♣10 was led and down went the dummy.

'Yes, that's not too bad,' Brother Aelred observed. He won the club lead in his hand and led a spade towards dummy, intending to finesse the jack. When West showed out, discarding a diamond, Brother Aelred shook his head disapprovingly and played dummy's ♠A.

'Perhaps I'll have better luck from the diamonds,' said Brother Aelred, as he led a low diamond from dummy. It was not to be. The black-bearded Brother Zac showed out on the first round of diamonds, discarding a spade. Once more Brother Aelred abandoned his plans for a finesse and won with the ace of the suit.

Since there was no future in playing on either spades or diamonds, Brother Aelred cashed three more rounds of clubs, followed by two of his top hearts. These cards remained:

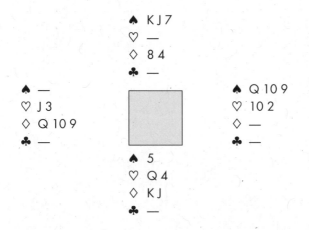

```
              ♠ K J 7
              ♡ —
              ◇ 8 4
              ♣ —
  ♠ —                        ♠ Q 10 9
  ♡ J 3        ┌──────┐      ♡ 10 2
  ◇ Q 10 9     │      │      ◇ —
  ♣ —          └──────┘      ♣ —
              ♠ 5
              ♡ Q 4
              ◇ K J
              ♣ —
```

Both the defenders could see the risk of being thrown in with a heart to lead into one of the king-jack tenaces. The indignity of being endplayed by so lowly a player as Brother Aelred was not to be contemplated; they had therefore taken the precaution of retaining their lowest spot-cards in hearts.

When Brother Aelred led the ♡Q from his hand, West followed with the jack and East produced the ten. Brother Aelred had not been counting the heart suit but the appearance of these high hearts rather suggested that there might be no more hearts out. He tested his luck with the ♡4 and this gathered the three and the two. With ten tricks already before him, Brother Aelred added the spade and diamond kings to his total. The slam was his.

'You did well to make four heart tricks, partner,' exclaimed Brother Sextus. 'Not that I was following the play very closely.'

'It wasn't difficult, really,' Brother Aelred replied. 'West had to guard the spades, East had to guard the diamonds, so no one could keep a heart guard. A perfect double squeeze!'

```
              ♠ A 5
              ♡ Q 7 5 2
              ◇ A J 7 2
              ♣ K J 3
♠ —                          ♠ Q J 10 9 6 3 2
♡ J 10 9 8                   ♡ 4
◇ Q 9 8 3                    ◇ 10 5 4
♣ 10 8 6 5 2                 ♣ 9 7
              ♠ K 8 7 4
              ♡ A K 6 3
              ◇ K 6
              ♣ A Q 4
```

West	North	East	South
		3♠	3NT
pass	6NT	all pass	

You win the ♡J lead with the ♡A and count ten top tricks. The hearts are unlikely to break 3-2, so you will need the ◇Q onside to bump your total to eleven tricks. To make a twelfth trick, you will have to set up a red-suit squeeze against West or a spade-diamond squeeze against East.

You need to rectify the count, so you lead a spade from your hand at Trick 2, ducking in dummy when West discards. You win the spade return and play a heart to the king, confirming the 4-1 break. After playing the ◇K, you finesse the ◇J and throw a heart on the ◇A. You then play three top clubs, ending in the South hand. East shows out, revealing his 7-1-3-2 shape, and these cards remain:

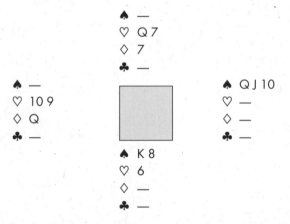

```
              ♠ —
              ♡ Q 7
              ◇ 7
              ♣ —
♠ —                          ♠ Q J 10
♡ 10 9                       ♡ —
◇ Q                          ◇ —
♣ —                          ♣ —
              ♠ K 8
              ♡ 6
              ◇ —
              ♣ —
```

The ♠K squeezes West in the red suits and the slam is yours. If East's shape turns out to be 7-1-4-1 instead, you cash the heart winners, followed by the clubs. Provided West has the ◇Q, this will squeeze East in spades and diamonds.

37. GISBURNE'S FEEBLE DEFENSE

Given an opportunity to swell his coffers, the Sheriff of Nottingham would let nothing stand in his way. On the present occasion Lord and Lady Barcliffe were visiting the castle. Their wealth was legendary and the Sheriff had treated them to a heavy roast venison luncheon, washed down with Spanish wine, before steering them to the rubber bridge table. Even partnered by his hopeless sidekick, Sir Guy of Gisburne, he would surely extract a substantial sum from the couple.

'We usually play for five guineas a hundred,' declared the Sheriff. 'A mere trifle for those in our fortunate position.'

'My Lord!' Gisburne protested. 'You know full well that five shillings is my limit. I really cannot...'

Gisburne was silenced by a kick on the shins and the blackest of glares from across the table. The message was clear. The Sheriff would stand his losses, should the unthinkable happen. Gisburne would be expected to play at his very best, meanwhile, to separate as much money as possible from this wealthy couple.

The first rubber had reached Game All when the ermine-clad Lord Barcliffe arrived in a slam. With a grim expression the Sheriff gathered his concentration. If the slam was allowed to make, it would not be at all the start to the proceedings that he had visualized. The cards lay like this:

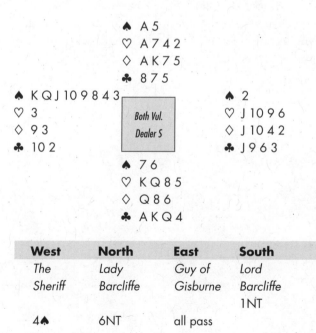

```
                  ♠ A 5
                  ♡ A 7 4 2
                  ◇ A K 7 5
                  ♣ 8 7 5
♠ K Q J 10 9 8 4 3              ♠ 2
♡ 3            ┌─────────┐      ♡ J 10 9 6
◇ 9 3         │ Both Vul. │     ◇ J 10 4 2
♣ 10 2        │ Dealer S  │     ♣ J 9 6 3
              └─────────┘
                  ♠ 7 6
                  ♡ K Q 8 5
                  ◇ Q 8 6
                  ♣ A K Q 4
```

West	North	East	South
The	Lady	Guy of	Lord
Sheriff	Barcliffe	Gisburne	Barcliffe
			1NT
4♠	6NT	all pass	

Lady Barcliffe was a very small woman, who had adopted a spiraling hairstyle to restore herself to average height. When the ♠K was led, she laid out the dummy and smiled conspiratorially at her husband. 'The stake money means nothing to us, of course,' she said. 'I thought it would be more fun for you to play in a slam, my love.'

Gisburne swallowed hard. A vulnerable slam at five-guinea stakes might mean nothing to them. By the Saints, it represented half a year's salary to him! It was just as well the Sheriff would be covering any losses.

Lord Barcliffe paused to assess his prospects. There were ten tricks on top — eleven if the heart suit broke 3-2. It was unlikely that either minor suit would divide equally, but perhaps he could squeeze East in the minors for a twelfth trick. Yes, there was nothing like a squeeze after a hearty lunch. Now, how could he rectify the count?

Lord Barcliffe leaned across the table and detached dummy's ♠5, allowing West's king to win the first trick. The Sheriff, who had little idea of squeezeplay, eyed his opponent scornfully. What in Heaven's name was the point of holding up the ace?

The spade continuation was won with dummy's ace and Gisburne spent some time considering his discard. As the seconds ticked by, the Sheriff became more and more agitated. If Gisburne made some foolish discard and handed them the slam on a plate, he could spend a night in the dungeons — commanding officer of the castle militia or not.

'That's very awkward, my Lord,' said Gisburne. Eventually he decided to match the length of the four-card suits in the dummy, discarding a club.

When Lord Barcliffe tested the heart suit, playing the ace and king, the Sheriff showed out on the second round. Declarer continued with his three top clubs, leaving these cards to be played:

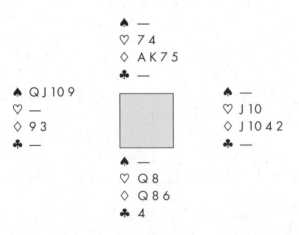

The Sheriff could not believe it when Barcliffe produced the ♣4. 'You blithering idiot, Gisburne!' he cried. 'Is it beyond your abilities to keep a guard on the club suit?'

A heart was thrown from the dummy and Gisburne sat motionless in his seat. What could he throw? A heart would definitely cost a trick, so he would have to discard a diamond, hoping that the Sheriff held the ◊Q.

Lord Barcliffe nodded happily when a diamond appeared. He cashed the queen, ace and king of the suit and claimed his twelfth trick with dummy's ◊7. The slam had been made.

The Sheriff rose angrily to his feet. 'You give them a club trick *and* a diamond trick?' he cried. 'I have rarely witnessed such a lamb-brained defense.'

'What would you have me do, my Lord?' stuttered Gisburne. 'If my first discard is a diamond, he plays four rounds of that suit.'

'You can pay your own losses on the session,' declared the Sheriff. 'That will concentrate your mind. Let's see if you fritter tricks away then.'

Barcliffe added up the rubber. 'It's not an amount to concern any of us,' he announced. 'One hundred and five guineas each, I make it.'

'We'll settle up at the end,' snapped the Sheriff. 'Draw a card to determine the dealer for the next rubber, Gisburne! A simple task like that isn't beyond you, is it?'

Quiz 21 *How would you play 6NT?*

♠ K 9
♡ 4 3
◊ A K Q 6 2
♣ K Q 5 3

♣10 led

♠ A 5 3 2
♡ A Q 6
◊ 10 4
♣ A J 4 2

West	North	East	South
			1NT
pass	6NT	all pass	

How will you tackle the notrump slam when West leads the ♣10? **(The answer is on page 110.)**

38. THE ABBOT JUMPS THE GUN

At half-time the scores were level in the county league match between the monastery and the local police station. The Abbot, none too pleased at having to play in a couple of dingy police cells, had been in a bad mood all evening.

'Must you smoke?' grunted the Abbot, as Inspector Bulstrode and Detective Sergeant Winter returned. 'These cells seem to have no ventilation at all.'

'They are a bit lacking in the basic comforts,' the Inspector replied, sending a column of smoke rings towards the ceiling. 'I thought you'd be used to that sort of thing, being monks.'

Battle recommenced and this was the big hand of the second half:

```
              ♠ A K 10 8 3
              ♡ A K J
              ◊ 7 5 2
              ♣ Q 6
♠ J 9 7 6 2                    ♠ 4
♡ 8 7 5        Both Vul.       ♡ 10 6 3 2
◊ Q 10 8 3     Dealer S        ◊ J 9 4
♣ 10                           ♣ K J 8 7 5
              ♠ Q 5
              ♡ Q 9 4
              ◊ A K 6
              ♣ A 9 4 3 2
```

West	North	East	South
Inspector	Brother	Det. Sgt.	The
Bulstrode	Xavier	Winter	Abbot
			1NT
pass	2♡	pass	2♠
pass	5NT	pass	6♣
pass	6NT	all pass	

Brother Xavier showed his five-card spade suit and then bid a 'pick a slam' 5NT to investigate a spade fit. The Abbot offered 6♣ as a contract and eventually settled in 6NT, West leading the ♡8.

The Abbot inspected the dummy, observing that the slam was somewhat less than cold. He won the heart lead in his hand and led a club to the ten, queen and king. The detective on his right was quick to return a club, hoping to put the Abbot to a decision in the suit before he knew the spade distribution.

On the present deal the Abbot needed two club tricks, even if the spade suit was coming in. The Principle of Restricted Choice made it more likely that the

♣10 was a singleton than a chosen card from ♣J10. The Abbot therefore inserted the ♣9, West discarding a heart. With East holding the club length, it was likely that West was long in spades. The Abbot therefore cashed the ♠Q and finessed dummy's ♠10 on the second round. East showed out on this trick, discarding a heart.

'In that case the rest are mine,' declared the Abbot, facing his cards with a flourish. These cards remained:

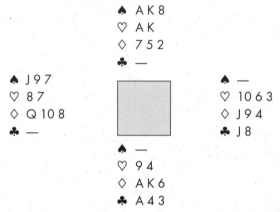

```
                    ♠ A K 8
                    ♡ A K
                    ◇ 7 5 2
                    ♣ —
    ♠ J 9 7                           ♠ —
    ♡ 8 7                             ♡ 10 6 3
    ◇ Q 10 8                          ◇ J 9 4
    ♣ —                               ♣ J 8
                    ♠ —
                    ♡ 9 4
                    ◇ A K 6
                    ♣ A 4 3
```

Inspector Bulstrode surveyed the evidence suspiciously. 'Four spades, three hearts, two diamonds and two clubs,' he said. 'That's a total of eleven tricks. Plus 100 to us, I make it.'

'Must I spell it out?' demanded the Abbot. 'When I cross to the diamond ace and cash the ace of clubs and the two top hearts, you must keep the spades, so you have to reduce to one diamond.'

The Inspector listened attentively, pretending he could follow the analysis.

'When I cash the two top spades,' continued the Abbot, 'the detective here must keep the clubs guarded. He, too, has to reduce to one diamond. Nobody, therefore can hold on to two diamonds. Except for myself, of course. It's the simplest conceivable non-simultaneous double squeeze.'

The Inspector, who had never understood squeezes, nodded his agreement. 'Had to get a full statement from you, Abbot,' he said. 'The er… doubled squeeze stood out a mile, as you say, but we always go through the formalities here.'

The match drew to a close and the monastery team had won by a satisfactory margin. 'Best of luck in the other league matches,' said the Inspector, as the Abbot waved farewell from the window of his dilapidated Morris Minor, 'to your opponents,' he added, under his breath.

As the car pulled out of the police yard, the Inspector could not believe his luck. 'Just a minute!' he cried. 'Your offside rear light's not working!'

The Abbot crunched into second gear and vanished round the corner.

'Into the Rover, lads,' shouted the Inspector, making good ground across the yard. 'We'll have him back in those cells in no time!'

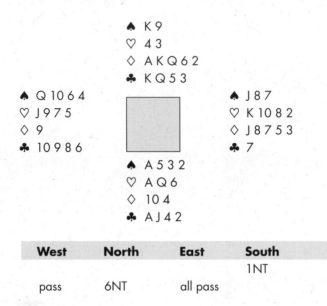

	♠ K 9	
	♡ 4 3	
	◊ A K Q 6 2	
	♣ K Q 5 3	
♠ Q 10 6 4		♠ J 8 7
♡ J 9 7 5		♡ K 10 8 2
◊ 9		◊ J 8 7 5 3
♣ 10 9 8 6		♣ 7
	♠ A 5 3 2	
	♡ A Q 6	
	◊ 10 4	
	♣ A J 4 2	

West	North	East	South
			1NT
pass	6NT	all pass	

North's policy is to waste as little energy as possible in the auction, keeping his brain fresh so that he can spot any errors in your declarer play. How will you play 6NT when West leads the ♣10?

There are ten tricks on top. If your first move is to cash the ◊A and ◊K to have a look at that suit, you will be defeated by the bad break. You cannot tell how to play the diamond suit until you know how many heart tricks you have. After winning the club lead in dummy, you should play a heart to the queen.

When the finesse wins, you have eleven top tricks and therefore need only four diamond tricks to make the slam. You return to dummy with a club to the queen and lead a low diamond towards the ten. Since East holds the ◊J, you will score four diamond tricks despite the 5-1 break. Suppose East rises with the ◊J and switches to a spade. You will win with the ♠A, preserving the spade entry to dummy. You then unblock the ◊10 and return to dummy with the ♠K to enjoy three more diamond tricks.

If the ♡Q lost to the ♡K, you would play the diamonds differently. Needing a full five tricks from the suit, you would play dummy's top honors and hope for a 3-3 break.

39. WITCHDOCTOR TO THE RESCUE

It was the last session of the Mrukash Challenge match between the Zbolwumba and the Bozwambi tribes. Things had not been going well at the Witchdoctor's table, where his overbidding had resulted in two sizable penalties. For the first time in ten years, it seemed that there was a serious danger of losing to their much-hated rivals.

Such a disgrace was not to be contemplated and the Witchdoctor regarded it as his personal responsibility to rescue the situation. Sitting South, at Love All, he thumbed through these cards:

♠ — ♡ 9 8 6 3 ◇ K 8 3 ♣ K J 10 9 7 2

East, the elderly Mr. Falimar, opened the bidding with one spade.

'One notrump!' said the Witchdoctor in an aggressive tone.

West paused briefly, presumably considering a bid, but then passed. It was now Brother Tobias's turn to speak. The Witchdoctor was not too worried. He was rather hoping that his partner would bid 2♣, which they played as Stayman in this sequence. He would then be left to play there! That would be amusing. Anyhow, surely Brother Tobias had noticed West's hesitation and would therefore bid with discretion. What was the harm of bidding 2♣ on the way to 3NT? Even if he did not hold four hearts, it was obviously the safest move in this situation.

'Six notrump,' said Brother Tobias.

'Double,' said Mr. Falimar.

The Witchdoctor rolled his eyes in disbelief. 'Mbaggar bfitsu!' he exclaimed, unable to restrain himself. 'Wah ennah boudani en Bwana brakash stufdada!'

'Come again?' said Brother Tobias, leaning forward.

There was no further bidding and this was the full deal:

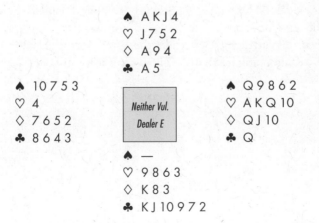

West	North	East	South
Mrs.	Brother	Mr.	Witch-
Falimar	Tobias	Falimar	doctor
		1♠	1NT
pass	6NT	dbl	all pass

Seeing no reason to ignore her husband's opening bid, Mrs. Falimar led the ♠3. The Witchdoctor rose with dummy's ♠A and continued with the ♣A, a welcome ♣Q appearing on his right. He cashed three more clubs to reach this position:

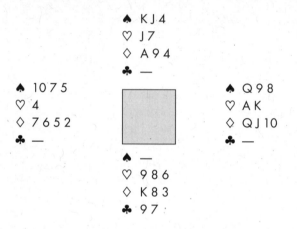

♠ K J 4
♡ J 7
◇ A 9 4
♣ —

♠ 10 7 5   ♠ Q 9 8
♡ 4   ♡ A K
◇ 7 6 5 2   ◇ Q J 10
♣ —   ♣ —

♠ —
♡ 9 8 6
◇ K 8 3
♣ 9 7

The Witchdoctor led the ♣9, throwing a heart from dummy. Mr. Falimar surveyed his remaining cards uneasily in the East seat. A further heart discard would allow declarer to set up two tricks in the suit. A diamond discard would give declarer an immediate extra trick in the suit and result in a throw-in play later. He glared across the table. Why hadn't Bettina led a heart? How could she lead partner's suit after a Lightner Double? Hoping for the best, Mr. Falimar discarded the ♠8.

The Witchdoctor now played his last club, throwing the ♠4 from dummy. When Mr Falimar discarded another spade, the Witchdoctor crossed to the ◇A and cashed the ♠K, dropping East's ♠Q. These cards were still out:

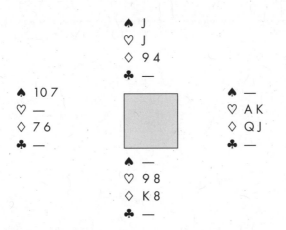

```
              ♠ J
              ♡ J
              ◇ 9 4
              ♣ —
♠ 10 7                      ♠ —
♡ —                        ♡ A K
◇ 7 6                      ◇ Q J
♣ —                        ♣ —
              ♠ —
              ♡ 9 8
              ◇ K 8
              ♣ —
```

On the ♠J East threw the ♡K. With an exultant sniff, the Witchdoctor threw the ◇8 and led dummy's ♡J to set up his twelfth trick. The slam was home.

'You were a bit light there,' observed Brother Tobias.

'How's I knowin' you go leapin' into sky like looney-man?' remonstrated the Witchdoctor. 'You had four hearts. Why you not biddin' Stayman?'

'You don't do very well in 6♡,' said Mr. Falimar, turning to address Brother Tobias. 'I had the hearts sitting over you.'

'Much safer in 6NT,' declared the Witchdoctor. 'Mind you, heart lead might be nasty. I think dat breakin' up de squeeze!'

Quiz 22 *How would you play 6NT?*

```
              ♠ J 3
              ♡ K 8 4
              ◇ K 10 6 3
              ♣ A Q 7 4
♡Q led        ┌──────────┐
              ♠ A K 7 5
              ♡ A 2
              ◇ A Q 4
              ♣ K J 9 2
```

West	North	East	South
			2NT
pass	6NT	all pass	

What's your plan when West leads the ♡Q? **(The answer is on page 116.)**

40. BROTHER CAMERON'S OBSERVATION

'Your hair needs cutting,' the Abbot informed Brother Cameron, as the novice arrived at the table and flung himself into the South seat. 'I told you that a couple of days ago.' He looked across at Brother Xavier, who performed the role of monastery barber. 'Did he come to see you?'

'I thought it would be all right if I combed it a different way,' the novice observed.

'Don't be absurd,' declared the Abbot. 'You will report to Brother Xavier immediately after Matins tomorrow. Don't just trim off half an inch, Xavier. Make the boy look neat and tidy for a change.'

The players drew their cards for this board:

```
                    ♠ K 10 7
                    ♡ A Q 10 4
                    ◇ A Q
                    ♣ 10 7 5 2
     ♠ 8 6 3                          ♠ 9 4 2
     ♡ J 6          Both Vul.         ♡ 9 7 3 2
     ◇ K J 7 2      Dealer S          ◇ 9 8 5 4
     ♣ A J 9 3                        ♣ 6 4
                    ♠ A Q J 5
                    ♡ K 8 5
                    ◇ 10 6 3
                    ♣ K Q 8
```

West	North	East	South
The	Brother	Brother	Brother
Abbot	Damien	Xavier	Cameron
			1NT
pass	2♣	pass	2♠
pass	4NT	pass	5◇
pass	6NT	all pass	

The Abbot led the ♠3 and down went the dummy. He turned towards Brother Cameron. 'Your partner's 4NT was a limit bid, not Roman Keycard,' he informed him. 'Why I bother giving bidding lessons to the novitiate, I really don't know. I covered that sequence only two weeks ago.'

'I knew it was a limit bid,' said Brother Cameron.

With 10 points in his own hand, the Abbot could tell that the novice was lying to him. He could hardly accuse him of this immediately or he would give away the position of the high cards.

'Play the ten of spades,' said Brother Cameron. He continued with a club to the king and ace, the Abbot returning a second round of spades. The young declarer won in his hand and finessed the ◊Q successfully. Four rounds of hearts and one more round of spades brought him to this end position:

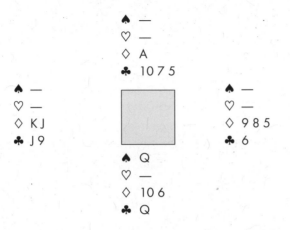

Brother Cameron played his last spade winner, putting the Abbot to a further discard. If he threw the ♣9, declarer would be able to cash the ♣Q and reach dummy with a diamond to enjoy the established ♣10.

Hoping that his partner held the ◊10, the Abbot decided to release the ◊J instead. Brother Cameron played a diamond to the ace and returned to his hand with the ♣Q to score his twelfth trick with the ◊10.

'Wow, a criss-cross squeeze!' exclaimed Brother Damien. 'Well played, partner.'

'That sort of thing happens to me time and again,' declared the Abbot. 'An absurd auction leading to an even more absurd contract. Then the cards lie so favorably that the contract falls into declarer's lap.'

'I may be wrong, Abbot,' said Brother Cameron, 'but what happens if you hold off your ace of clubs at Trick 2?'

The Abbot pretended not to hear, studying the point of his pencil and then scribbling something indecipherable on the back of his scorecard.

'I don't think I can do it then,' continued Brother Cameron. 'In fact I'd probably try leading towards the queen of clubs and go two down.'

'Did someone speak?' said the Abbot, glaring in turn at Brother Cameron and Brother Damien. 'Gloating over a lucky result is not the way we do things here at St. Titus. Bring up the next board, will you?'

                        ♠ J 3
                        ♡ K 8 4
                        ◇ K 10 6 3
                        ♣ A Q 7 4

    ♠ 9 8 4   ♠ Q 10 6 2
    ♡ Q J 10 7 3   ♡ 9 6 5
    ◇ 8 5   ◇ J 9 7 2
    ♣ 10 8 6   ♣ 5 3

                        ♠ A K 7 5
                        ♡ A 2
                        ◇ A Q 4
                        ♣ K J 9 2

West	North	East	South
			2NT
pass	6NT	all pass	

How will you play 6NT when West leads the ♡Q?

You have eleven tricks on top and the diamond suit offers a good chance of a twelfth trick. There is no need to rely exclusively on a favorable diamond position. You should win the heart lead with the ace and lead low towards dummy's ♠J. When West holds the ♠Q, you will make a third spade trick and can claim twelve tricks before you even look at the diamond position. Many players have a blind spot with this particular spade holding.

When the cards lie as in the diagram, the ♠J loses to East's ♠Q. You win the spade return and cash your heart and club winners. This will be the end position:

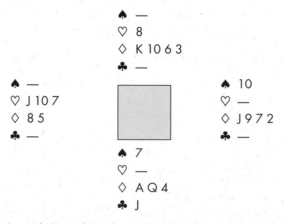

                        ♠ —
                        ♡ 8
                        ◇ K 10 6 3
                        ♣ —

    ♠ —   ♠ 10
    ♡ J 10 7   ♡ —
    ◇ 8 5   ◇ J 9 7 2
    ♣ —   ♣ —

                        ♠ 7
                        ♡ —
                        ◇ A Q 4
                        ♣ J

You play the ♣J, discarding dummy's ♡8. East cannot throw the ♠10 without setting up your ♠7. Nor will he fare any better by throwing a diamond. You will then score four diamond tricks in the dummy.

41. MADAME BAGUETTE'S ANALYSIS

The Matron surveyed the two fourth-formers disapprovingly as they took their seats. They had been perfectly clean and presentable at morning inspection. How was it possible for them to look so scruffy just a few hours later?

'Is anything the matter, Matron?' John Hutson enquired.

'Both of you look a complete mess,' the Matron replied. 'Your parents would be ashamed of you.'

'Mine are on holiday in Kenya, actually,' Hutson replied. 'Absolutely typical. They take me and my sister to some grotty bed-and-breakfast in Cornwall and then, during term time, they go on safari.'

'I don't care if your parents are in Timbuktu,' retorted the Matron. 'That's no excuse for presenting yourselves in such a state. I dare say the Headmaster will have something to say about it.'

'We played him on the last round, Matron,' said Neil Phillips. 'He didn't say a word.'

Letting the matter drop, the Matron drew her cards for the first board of the round:

```
              ♠ A 3
              ♡ 8 6 2
              ◇ K J 9 7
              ♣ A K 6 3
♠ 10 8 6 5 2                  ♠ 7 4
♡ 3           Both Vul.       ♡ K Q J 9 5 4
◇ 10 5 3 2    Dealer E        ◇ 6 4
♣ Q 8 2                       ♣ J 9 5
              ♠ K Q J 9
              ♡ A 10 7
              ◇ A Q 8
              ♣ 10 7 4
```

West	North	East	South
Madame	Neil	The	John
Baguette	Phillips	Matron	Hutson
		2♡	2NT
pass	6NT	all pass	

The Matron opened with a weak two-bid and the two youngsters propelled themselves into 6NT. The ♡3 was led and Neil Phillips displayed his dummy. 'Not the moment for you to have a queen-high heart stopper, I realize,' he said.

The Matron produced the ♡J and Hutson won with the ace. A count of his top tricks, followed by a recount when the first total proved unsatisfactory, revealed that he was one trick short. The only chance he could see for a twelfth trick was to find a 3-3 club break. Of course, it would be no good if the Matron won a club trick because she would have several hearts to cash.

Hutson marked time by cashing four rounds of diamonds, throwing a heart from his hand. He had been hoping to see a club discard from the Matron but she threw two low spades instead. What now? Perhaps he could lead a club to the ten? If Madame Baguette held QJx in the suit she would have to win the first round of clubs and would then have no heart to play. 'Low club, please,' said John Hutson.

The Matron followed with the ♣5 and declarer's ♣10 was won by West's queen. As expected, Madame Baguette had no heart to play. Hutson won the club return in dummy and claimed the contract when clubs proved to be 3-3.

'Were you asleep, Matron?' cried an exasperated Madame Baguette. 'Put up the jack of clubs and you can cash five heart tricks!'

'A double-dummy defense if ever I heard one,' replied the Matron. 'I placed declarer with the queen of clubs.'

'Yes, but how can it cost to rise with the jack?' persisted Madame Baguette. 'The ace and king were in the dummy.'

Neil Phillips opened the score-sheet and was surprised to find that there was one 1440 already on display. 'It can't be that easy to put in the jack of clubs,' he said. 'Bertie Bellis made 6NT too.'

Madame Baguette raised her eyes to the ceiling. 'An excellent player like Bertie will have played the clubs properly,' she said. 'Lead twice towards the ace-king, ducking if the queen comes. Do that and it is easy to keep the Matron off lead.'

John Hutson's mouth fell open. Good gracious, Madame Baguette was right! If she played low on the first two rounds of clubs, she would have to win the third round with the queen.

The Matron, who had made no attempt to follow this analysis, nodded her head wisely. 'Quite right, partner,' she said. 'These youngsters have such a lot to learn from us more experienced players.'

42. THE ABBOT'S UNFORTUNATE LEAD

For most teams, the prime attraction of entering the Hampshire Knockout Cup was that national green masterpoints were awarded for each match. The Abbot had been a Grandmaster for over ten years, as he never tired of telling people. Nevertheless, he still liked to accumulate green points. 'Think what will happen in a hundred years time, when the players look back at our generation,' he would say. 'How can they judge who were the truly great players? All they will have to go by is the green point records.'

There were mixed feelings all round when the draw for the second round of the Knockout Cup placed the senior St. Titus team against Brother Cameron's team from the novitiate. The Abbot was putting a brave face on it, claiming that it would be like scoring half a green point for getting out of bed. Privately, he knew that the senior team was on a hiding to nothing. If they won the match, even by a large margin, so what? And if Lucius and Paulo had one of their bad sessions and the senior team were actually to lose? Well, it didn't bear thinking about.

Since the novices normally went to bed an hour earlier than the senior monks, the Abbot arranged a fairly late starting time of eight o'clock. By his reckoning, the novices should be feeling quite sleepy by half-time and would then start to make some serious mistakes.

The novices had seating rights in the first set and it was no surprise when their captain, Brother Cameron, chose to face the Abbot. This was an early board at Lucius and Paulo's table:

```
                    ♠ J 5 2
                    ♡ 10 8 6 5
                    ◇ 6 5
                    ♣ A J 5 2
    ♠ 6                            ♠ 10 9 8 7 4 3
    ♡ J 9 3 2        EW Vul.       ♡ 7 4
    ◇ Q J 10 9 8 4   Dealer S      ◇ —
    ♣ 8 3                          ♣ 10 9 7 6 4
                    ♠ A K Q
                    ♡ A K Q
                    ◇ A K 7 3 2
                    ♣ K Q
```

West	North	East	South
Brother	Brother	Brother	Brother
Adam	Lucius	Mark	Paulo
			2♣
pass	2◇	pass	4NT
pass	6NT	all pass	

Brother Paulo decided not to mention his diamonds, preferring a straightforward limit rebid of 4NT. Lucius raised him to a small slam and the ◊Q was led.

'Very nice, partner,' said Brother Paulo, as the dummy appeared. It was known throughout the monastery that this remark gave away nothing whatsoever. Brother Paulo delivered the same three words, in an unvarying monotone, whether the contract was lay-down or had no play.

Eyebrows were raised around the table as East showed out on the diamond lead, discarding a spade. Paulo won with the ◊A and marked time by cashing two rounds of spades. Further information came to light when West showed out on the second round, throwing a diamond. When the three top hearts were played, the jack refused to fall and East discarded another spade on the third round. Paulo sat back in his chair. He had an easy eleven tricks by overtaking on the second round of clubs. How could he make a twelfth trick?

Brother Paulo soon found the answer. West held the guards in both red suits, so he would be squeezed if a black-suit winner could be played from the dummy. He cashed the ♣K and overtook the ♣Q with dummy's ace. These cards remained to be played:

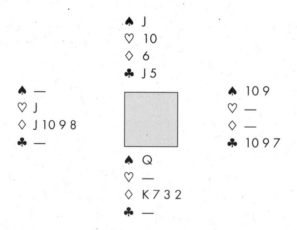

'Club five, please,' said Brother Paulo.

East won the trick and the Italian monk flipped the ♠Q onto the table. The novice in the West seat discarded a diamond and his partner then had to play one or other black suit, giving the lead to dummy. West threw another diamond on the club return. When Brother Paulo cashed dummy's remaining winner, the ♠J, West had no card to spare. If he discarded the ♡J, dummy's ♡10 would be good. He chose instead to throw yet another diamond and Paulo claimed the last two tricks with the ◊K and ◊7 in his hand.

'Wow!' said Brother Adam. 'You played that well.'

Brother Paulo smiled at his young opponent. 'Not so difficult when you know where all the cards are,' he replied. 'It's strange but a 6-0 diamond break was more helpful to me than a 4-2 break.'

Brother Adam did not follow the exact point being made but was happy to share a conversation with his one of his biggest heroes. 'Yes, indeed,' he said.

Back at the Abbot's table, Brother Cameron had just arrived in 6NT on a different board. This was the layout:

```
                      ♠ J 6
                      ♡ K 5
                      ◇ 7 6 4 2
                      ♣ A K 6 3 2

  ♠ 10 8 4 3      ┌─────────────┐      ♠ Q 9 5 2
  ♡ Q J 10 9 2    │  Both Vul.  │      ♡ 8 6 3
  ◇ —             │             │      ◇ 10 9 8 5 3
  ♣ Q J 9 5       │  Dealer S   │      ♣ 8
                  └─────────────┘
                      ♠ A K 7
                      ♡ A 7 4
                      ◇ A K Q J
                      ♣ 10 7 4
```

West	North	East	South
The	Brother	Brother	Brother
Abbot	Damien	Xavier	Cameron
			2NT
pass	4NT	pass	6NT
all pass			

For a moment the Abbot was tempted to double 6NT. The auction indicated that declarer would have few values to spare and all the suits were breaking badly. Still, if Brother Cameron made 6NT doubled against him, the story would reverberate around the novitiate for weeks. Better to play safe and pass. At least he had the world's most obvious opening lead.

The Abbot led the ♡Q and Brother Cameron won in hand with the ace. To make the contract, it seemed that he would have to score four club tricks. What were the possibilities? Suppose he led low to dummy's ace and West produced a singleton queen or jack. He would not be able to make the slam. If he tried a low club towards the ten next, East would fly in with his honor and remove dummy's ♡K while the clubs were blocked.

What if East held a singleton club? There was no way to deal with a singleton queen or jack, because the defenders would then have two certain tricks in the suit.

'Come on, come on,' exclaimed the Abbot. 'I wouldn't have set an eight o'clock start time if I knew you were going to play so slowly. It's only a local match, not the Gold Cup.'

'Sorry, Abbot,' said Brother Cameron.

The novice eventually concluded that unless clubs were 3-2, he would need to find East with a singleton eight or nine. With this in mind, he led the ♣10 from his hand. Not liking the look of this much, the Abbot covered with the ♣J. Brother Cameron won with dummy's ace and noted with interest the appearance of the ♣8 on his right.

When a second round of clubs was led from dummy, East showed out and Brother Cameron played the seven from his hand. The Abbot had no counter to this. If he won with the queen or nine, a subsequent finesse of dummy's ♣6 would give declarer the contract. If instead he allowed the ♣7 to win, declarer would simply continue with king and another club, setting up a long card while the ♡K entry was still intact.

'I must make four club tricks,' said Brother Cameron, facing his remaining cards by way of claiming the contract.

The Abbot gave a reluctant nod of the head and returned his cards to the wallet.

'Unfortunate lead, Abbot,' observed Brother Xavier. 'If you leave the heart entries intact, declarer might well start with a low club to the ace, hoping to pick up single queen or jack in your hand.'

The Abbot looked wearily across the table. Even by Brother Xavier's standards, this was a fatuous observation. 'I've never heard such nonsense,' he declared. 'Declarer will obviously cash some diamonds before he decides who to play for a possible club shortage. When I show out on the first round of diamonds it's obvious, even for a modest performer, that you're the favorite to hold a singleton club.'

'You may be right,' said Brother Xavier.

'Apart from that,' continued the Abbot, 'a queen of clubs lead from me would give the position away and who in their right mind would lead a spade from four to the ten when they had a solid sequence in hearts?'

'I didn't mean to find fault with your lead, Abbot,' replied Brother Xavier. 'I just said it was a bit unfortunate.'

'It was a good deal less unfortunate than some of the remarks you see fit to make during a match,' persisted the Abbot. 'Ah, Lucius and Paulo have finished. Time to score up the first set!'

Quiz 23 *How would you play 6NT?*

```
                        ♠ Q 5
                        ♡ A 10 2
                        ◇ A 8 7 3 2
                        ♣ A 7 4
        ♡5 led          ▭▭▭▭▭
                        ♠ K 4 3
                        ♡ K Q 9
                        ◇ K Q 6
                        ♣ K Q J 6
```

West	North	East	South
3♠	pass	pass	3NT
pass	4NT	pass	6NT
all pass			

North's 4NT invites a slam and you feel you have to accept with 19 points for your 3NT bid. How will you tackle the slam when West leads the ♡5? **(The answer is overleaf.)**

ANSWER TO **QUIZ 23** *(previous page)*

```
            ♠ Q 5
            ♡ A 10 2
            ◇ A 8 7 3 2
            ♣ A 7 4
♠ A J 10 8 7 6 2          ♠ 9
♡ 5 4 3                   ♡ J 8 7 6
◇ 9                       ◇ J 10 5 4
♣ 9 3                     ♣ 10 8 5 2
            ♠ K 4 3
            ♡ K Q 9
            ◇ K Q 6
            ♣ K Q J 6
```

West	North	East	South
3♠	pass	pass	3NT
pass	4NT	pass	6NT
all pass			

West selects the ♡5 as the safest lead on view and you win in the South hand. All follow to the ◇K but West shows out when you continue with the ◇Q. What now?

You have ten tricks on top, with a potential eleventh trick from the spade suit. You cannot simply clear yourself an extra trick from the diamonds, of course, since East would return a spade and you would then lose a diamond and a spade. What can be done?

You must lead a low spade towards dummy's queen. This is an example of the avoidance play known as Morton's Fork. If West goes in with the ♠A, you will have two spade tricks, enough to bring your total to twelve. If instead West holds off the ♠A, you will win with dummy's ♠Q. That will give you eleven top tricks and you will be able to set up the diamonds safely, because East's sole card in the spade suit has been stripped. When you duck a round of diamonds to East, he will have no spade to return.

43. THE RABBI'S LITTLE SECRET

Every Tuesday night, a duplicate pairs was held in the synagogue memorial hall.

Eric was looking worried as he took his seat opposite the Rabbi. 'Only seventh place last week,' he said. 'Such good television there is on a Tuesday. If we win or come second, I don't mind missing it.'

'You can record the programs, surely?' the Rabbi replied. 'A man like you must have the latest electronic device for recording.'

'Yes, of course, our digital hard-drive recorder,' said Eric. 'But it is absolutely full of programs. With so much work to do during the day, and so much bridge at night, I never have a chance to watch anything.'

The Rabbi nodded sympathetically. 'A sign of the times,' he observed.

Among the early visitors to the Rabbi's table were Miriam and her husband, the Cantor. 'Your hair looks different, Miriam,' the Rabbi observed. 'A new style for you?'

'Someone has noticed, that is good,' Miriam replied. She looked across the table, glaring at her husband. 'Not everyone is so observant.'

'It looks nice, it looks nice,' declared the Cantor. 'Do I have eyes in the back of my head? Can I see your hair when I am changing into some comfortable clothes for the bridge game?'

'You had been home for more than ten minutes before you noticed it,' Miriam reprimanded. 'Why I take such trouble to look nice, I don't know.'

This was the first board they played:

```
              ♠ 9 7 6
              ♡ K 8 6 4 2
              ◇ A 8
              ♣ 7 5 3
♠ 4                        ♠ K J 10 8 3 2
♡ J 10 7 5     Both Vul.   ♡ 9 3
◇ 10 9 3 2     Dealer E    ◇ J 5
♣ J 10 9 2                 ♣ 8 6 4
              ♠ A Q 5
              ♡ A Q
              ◇ K Q 7 6 4
              ♣ A K Q
```

West	North	East	South
Miriam	Eric	The	The
		Cantor	Rabbi
		2♠	dbl
pass	3♡	pass	6NT
all pass			

Deciding that her husband did not deserve a lead of his suit after such inattentive behavior, Miriam led the ♣J against 6NT. Down went the dummy and the Cantor surveyed it with some surprise. 'Not a single point he promises in the bidding, Rabbi,' he said, 'and he gives you an ace and a king!'

Miriam winced. Must he display his ignorance every time they play together? 'They use the Lebensohl convention, Ronnie,' she said. 'With a weak hand you respond 2NT. A suit bid shows values.'

'Lebensohl, you say?' queried the Cantor. 'That sounds like a good Jewish convention. Maybe we should play it.'

The Rabbi won with the ♣A and paused to consider his prospects. He had eleven tricks on top, assuming that the spade finesse would succeed. How could he combine his chances in the red suits? Suppose he cashed the ♡A and ♡Q, crossed to the ◇A and tried his luck with the ♡K. If hearts broke 4-2, it could then be dangerous to give up a diamond trick. West might have started with four diamonds and four hearts and would then cash a heart trick to put the slam one down. Ah yes, of course, he should duck a diamond while he still had protection in hearts.

The Rabbi cashed the ace and queen of hearts and led a diamond towards dummy. 'Eight, please,' he said.

Eric leaned forward. 'Ace, did you say, Rabbi?'

The Rabbi was in a mischievous mood. 'I meant to play the ace,' he replied. 'Ah well, too late, I called for the eight, I must admit.'

The Cantor won dummy's ◇8 with the ◇J and returned a club. The Rabbi won with the ♣K and crossed to the ◇A, everyone following. East showed out when the ♡K was played and the Rabbi discarded his low spade. When a finesse of the ♠Q proved successful, the slam was his.

'Playing the ◇8 didn't cost you, Rabbi,' the Cantor observed. 'With diamonds breaking 4-2, you would have had to give up a diamond anyway.'

The Rabbi maintained a straight face. 'Yes, yes, it was a lucky escape,' he replied. 'If only all such mistakes could end so happily.'

A round or two later, the strong partnership of Maurice Stone and Moishe Silverman arrived at the Rabbi's table. Although they usually finished in the top three positions, the Rabbi had a good record against them. 'How are tricks tonight, Moishe?' he asked.

'Can't complain,' Silverman replied. 'Two big gifts and one fix, so far. And you?'

'Ups and downs,' said the Rabbi.

Eric smiled. 'Yes, we bid up on every hand and then we go down.'

'Promises, promises,' said Maurice Stone. 'Shall we play?'

This was the deal before them:

```
                    ♠ A 10 5
                    ♡ K Q 7
                    ◇ A 8 3
                    ♣ A 7 4 2
  ♠ 9 7 3 2                          ♠ J 8 4
  ♡ 10 6 4      ┌──────────┐         ♡ 8 5 3 2
  ◇ Q J 10 5    │ Both Vul.│         ◇ 9 7 2
  ♣ K 3         │ Dealer S │         ♣ 10 8 6
                └──────────┘
                    ♠ K Q 6
                    ♡ A J 9
                    ◇ K 6 4
                    ♣ Q J 9 5
```

West	North	East	South
Stone	Eric	Silverman	The Rabbi
			1NT
pass	6NT	all pass	

Maurice Stone led the ◇Q and a respectable dummy hit the table. 'A nice hand for me, partner,' observed the Rabbi. 'Thank you.' It took the Rabbi only a couple of seconds to realize that the slam was poor. The only real chance was to score four club tricks. Ah well, it would be the same for the players at the other tables.

The Rabbi won the diamond lead with the king and advanced the ♣Q, drawing the ♣3 from West and the ♣8 from East. What now? If West had started with a doubleton ♣K, low to the ace would flush it out. If instead East had begun with ♣10-8, a lead of the ♣J on the second round would pin the ♣10.

The Rabbi considered carefully the spot cards he had seen on the first round. The ♣8 had appeared from East. Most declarers would conclude that East was likely to hold ♣10-8 doubleton. The Rabbi was not so sure. These particular opponents never missed the chance of a false card. Moishe Silverman would play the ♣8 from ♣1086 or ♣1083, as well being forced to play it from ♣10-8. The odds were therefore 2-to-1 in favor of playing him for three clubs.

The Rabbi turned to glance at Maurice Stone in the West seat. He had played the ♣3 on the first round. If he had started with ♣K63, a player like Maurice would surely have played a cunning ♣6, hoping to look like a player with a doubleton king. His actual ♣3 made it a near certainty that the ♣K was now bare!

'One needs a little luck in this world,' declared the Rabbi, playing the ♣5 from his hand. The ♣K appeared from West, much to the aggravation of both defenders and the Rabbi proceeded to claim his slam.

'How can you read the clubs, Rabbi?' demanded Silverman. 'Such a clever ♣8, I play. You did not think it was from ♣10-8 doubleton?'

'You played the eight, did you?' queried the Rabbi. 'I was looking only for the king or the ten. Small spot cards, I don't notice them!'

44. THE ABBOT'S WASTED HAND

'I make the rubber fifteen points,' declared the Abbot, shaking his head. 'Switch to the jack of diamonds, partner, and we live to fight another day.' He reached inside an old leather wallet, reluctantly extracting three £5 notes. 'Table up!' he cried.

The white-haired Brother Sextus, a very moderate player, approached the table. 'Are you coming in?' enquired the Abbot, in as discouraging a tone as he could muster.

'Just for one rubber, yes,' Brother Sextus replied.

The players cut to see who should make way for the new arrival. The Abbot took no part in this procedure, one of his long-established privileges allowing him to sit at the £1 table for as long as he wished. The draw for partners placed Brother Sextus in partnership with the Abbot and the rubber opened with this deal:

```
                    ♠ A K 4
                    ♡ K Q 9
                    ◇ K 9 7 6
                    ♣ A K Q
   ♠ 10 9 8 3                        ♠ 7 6 2
   ♡ A 4          Neither Vul.       ♡ J 7 3
   ◇ J 8 5 2       Dealer N          ◇ 10 4 3
   ♣ 10 7 3                          ♣ 8 6 5 2
                    ♠ Q J 5
                    ♡ 10 8 6 5 2
                    ◇ A Q
                    ♣ J 9 4
```

West	North	East	South
Brother	The	Brother	Brother
Lucius	Abbot	Xavier	Sextus
	2♣	pass	2NT
pass	3NT	pass	6NT
all pass			

The Abbot's joy at picking up a 24-count was somewhat diminished when Brother Sextus ended at the helm of the subsequent slam. Was it too much to ask that he might, just for once, give the contract the attention that it deserved?

The ♠10 was led and the Abbot was pleased to see Brother Sextus pause to make a plan before playing to the first trick. Now, thought Brother Sextus, how many top tricks were there? Oh dear, only nine. Well, maybe he could establish some more from dummy's heart suit. Since the first heart lead would have to be made towards the dummy, it made good sense to win the spade lead in his hand.

Brother Sextus won the first trick with the ♠Q and led a heart to the king, which won. He returned to his hand with the ◊Q and led another round of hearts, West rising with the ace. Brother Sextus's relief at the appearance of this card was quickly stemmed by the realization that the heart suit would be blocked if he played low from dummy. A diamond switch from West would then cut him off from the heart winners in his hand.

Brother Sextus surveyed dummy's cards unhappily. If East had started with a doubleton ♡J, he could untangle the suit by unblocking dummy's queen under West's ace; East's jack would fall and he would then be able to cross to the ten on the third round. Still, if West had started with ♡Axx, he might well have ducked twice to put declarer to a guess.

Eventually Brother Sextus played low from dummy, hoping that West would misdefend. Declarer's predicament was not lost on Brother Lucius in the West seat and he was quick to return a second round of diamonds. No miracle occurred when the last few tricks were played out and the slam went one down.

'A sad waste of my 24-count,' declared the Abbot. 'Why didn't you mention your hearts? Six hearts was frigid.'

'Just as frigid as 6NT, in fact,' said Brother Lucius. He turned towards the elderly declarer. 'You should win the spade lead in dummy, not in your hand. Then you can cross twice in diamonds to lead towards the heart honors. The hearts become blocked, as before, but I can't remove your spade entry.'

'It's not in my nature to criticize partner,' declared the Abbot, 'otherwise I would have pointed out the winning line myself.' He paused to make an illegible entry in the minus column of his scorepad. 'Win the opening lead in dummy, partner! I couldn't believe it when you played low.'

Quiz 24 *How will you play 6NT?*

```
              ♠ K Q J 7
              ♡ 10 8 7 5
              ◊ J 2
              ♣ Q 8 3
◊10 led       [                 ]
              ♠ A 5
              ♡ A K 9 3
              ◊ A K Q 4
              ♣ A 10 7
```

West	North	East	South
			2♣
pass	2◊	pass	2NT
pass	4NT	pass	6NT
all pass			

How would you play this slam when West leads the ◊10? **(The answer is overleaf.)**

```
                    ♠ K Q J 7
                    ♡ 10 8 7 5
                    ◇ J 2
                    ♣ Q 8 3
  ♠ 10 3 2                            ♠ 9 8 6 4
  ♡ Q J 6 4                           ♡ 2
  ◇ 10 9 7                            ◇ 8 6 5 3
  ♣ K 9 5                             ♣ J 6 4 2
                    ♠ A 5
                    ♡ A K 9 3
                    ◇ A K Q 4
                    ♣ A 10 7
```

West	North	East	South
			2♣
pass	2◇	pass	2NT
pass	4NT	pass	6NT
all pass			

West leads the ◇10 against 6NT. You have eleven top tricks and the club suit offers you a good chance of creating a twelfth trick. You could lead towards the ♣Q. If that lost to the ♣K with East, you could finesse the ♣10 on the next round. This line would in fact succeed against the lie of cards shown in the diagram, but it is not the best way to play the contract.

The heart suit offers better prospects of a twelfth trick. You win the diamond lead with dummy's jack and cross to the ♡A, both defenders following low. You then play a low heart towards dummy's ten. If hearts break 3-2, all will be easy. If East began with ♡QJxx, you can take a marked finesse on the third round. Only when West holds ♡QJxx will the contract still be in doubt. (The chance of this happening is only about half that of the 'two club finesse' line failing.)

With the cards lying as in the diagram, West will rise with the ♡J in second seat and East will show out. West then exits with a spade, which you win with the ace. What can you do now?

You can still make the contract if West also holds the ♣K. You must cash the ♣A, a Vienna Coup to set up dummy's ♣Q as an unfettered threat card. Next you cash your diamond winners, discarding a heart and a club from dummy. Finally you cash the remaining spade winners in dummy. On the last of these, West has to find one more discard from the ♡Q6 and the ♣K. If he unguards the clubs, dummy's ♣Q will score. If he throws a heart, your ♡9 will become the twelfth trick.

45. THE BISHOP OF LEICESTER'S WARNING

On the outskirts of Nottingham there were several taverns in which money rubber bridge was played. The richest pickings were available at the Crown and Pikestaff, north of the town, but it was a dangerous place for outlaws to visit.

Desperately in need of funds, Robin Hood had decided to take the risk. In a far corner of the smoky tavern he was immersed in a high-stake game with two fur traders and the Bishop of Leicester, whose enormous girth was wrapped in purple. The Bishop was a close ally of the Sheriff of Nottingham. If Robin were to be recognized, his life would be in peril.

'I say Two Clubs on this one,' declared Robin Hood.

This was the deal before them:

```
                    ♠ 5 4
                    ♡ 10 7 6 3
                    ◇ A J 8
                    ♣ 9 7 4 3
  ♠ Q J 9 8 6 3                      ♠ 7
  ♡ J 5          ┌──────────┐        ♡ 9 8 4 2
  ◇ 6            │ Both Vul.│        ◇ 10 9 7 3 2
  ♣ K 10 6 2     │ Dealer S │        ♣ J 8 5
                 └──────────┘
                    ♠ A K 10 2
                    ♡ A K Q
                    ◇ K Q 5 4
                    ♣ A Q
```

West	North	East	South
Bishop of Leicester	John of Kirkstall	Reuben Siegler	Robin Hood
			2♣
pass	2◇	pass	3NT
pass	6NT	all pass	

The Bishop of Leicester tossed the spade queen defiantly on to the gnarled oak table and down went the dummy. 'Not much there for me,' observed Robin Hood.

'First chance of a slam all night,' his partner replied. 'I'm nearly four pounds down on the session. I couldn't let a slam go by.'

Robin Hood won the first trick with the ♠A and played two top hearts. The jack fell from West on the second round and he continued with a third round.

'The luck of the Devil, you have!' the Bishop exclaimed. 'Your partner overbids like a madman and then my jack of hearts falls.'

Robin Hood assumed a pious expression. 'The Good Lord must have wished it that way,' he replied.

A successful club finesse would now be enough for the slam. Robin Hood cashed the ◊K and ◊J and was interested to see West show out on the second round. There was no need now to rely solely on the club finesse for the contract. These cards remained:

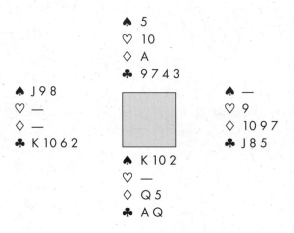

```
              ♠ 5
              ♡ 10
              ◊ A
              ♣ 9 7 4 3
♠ J 9 8                        ♠ —
♡ —                            ♡ 9
◊ —                            ◊ 10 9 7
♣ K 10 6 2                     ♣ J 8 5
              ♠ K 10 2
              ♡ —
              ◊ Q 5
              ♣ A Q
```

Robin Hood leaned forward to play dummy's ♠5. A glint came to his eye when East showed out on the trick, discarding a diamond. He followed with the ♠2 from his hand, throwing the Bishop of Leicester on lead.

Knowing that a spade return would surrender a trick, the Bishop tossed a low club on to the table. Robin Hood now had twelve tricks — four in each red suit, two in each black suit.

'Curse you and your luck!' cried the Bishop. 'I've rarely seen such a fortunate lie of the cards.'

The players had just settled up for the rubber when the Landlord, who was built like an ox, arrived at the table. 'What are the stakes here?' he demanded.

'A florin a hundred,' Hood replied. The Landlord made a note in a small black book and then left the table. 'Strange question to ask,' remarked Hood.

The Bishop of Leicester glared at him. 'You leather-brain!' he exclaimed. 'The table money here depends on the stakes. I told him we were playing for two pence a hundred.'

Robin Hood gave an apologetic shrug of the shoulders. 'That's a new idea, charging table money,' he said. 'We wouldn't take to that at the Drunken Pheasant.'

The Bishop twitched in his seat. 'Good grief, you play there?' he exclaimed. 'I've heard the place is swarming with outlaws.'

Robin Hood could not believe his indiscretion. 'Thank goodness you warned me, your Grace,' he replied. 'I'll keep well clear of the place in the future.'

46. SISTER BENEDICT'S CLEVER BID

The Mother of Discipline nodded approvingly as one of the Convent's least able pairs arrived at the table — Sister Myrtle and Sister Benedict. Sister Myrtle had always been a large woman but following the demise of her recent 'fruit and juice' diet, she had regained weight at an alarming rate. She played the first board in 4♣, a favorite stopping place of hers. The score sheet revealed that 3NT plus one had proved more popular elsewhere.

'Don't blame me,' exclaimed Sister Benedict. 'I could hardly risk 3NT with just four small spades in my hand.'

'I couldn't bid it either,' replied Sister Myrtle. 'I don't call three spades to the jack a reliable stopper, do you?'

'No, indeed,' said Sister Benedict. 'The hand was unbiddable, playing Acol.'

The players drew their cards for the second board of the round:

```
                      ♠ A K Q J 10 7
                      ♡ 5 3
                      ◇ A K 2
                      ♣ A 7
    ♠ 4                                   ♠ 9 6 5 3
    ♡ 10 4           Both Vul.            ♡ A K Q
    ◇ J 10 9 8 4 3   Dealer N             ◇ 7 5
    ♣ 9 8 6 4                             ♣ Q J 5 3
                      ♠ 8 2
                      ♡ J 9 8 7 6 2
                      ◇ Q 6
                      ♣ K 10 2
```

West	North	East	South
Mother of	*Sister*	*Sister*	*Sister*
Discipline	*Benedict*	*Thomas*	*Myrtle*
	2♠	pass	2NT
pass	4NT	pass	5♣
pass	6NT	all pass	

'You play strong two-bids?' enquired the Mother of Discipline, who was on lead.

'Oh yes, Reverend Mother,' Sister Benedict replied. 'No one would play weak two-bids when vulnerable, surely? We play them all the time, anyway.'

The Mother of Discipline led the ◇J and down went the dummy. 'Some would say that I should bid the slam in spades,' Sister Benedict observed. 'But when you denied an ace, the odds were good that you would hold the king of hearts. By getting you to play the contract, I could protect your king from the opening lead.'

Sister Myrtle surveyed the dummy uncertainly. Had she promised anything at all by her bidding? 'You have only nine tricks there, Sister,' she replied. 'Why should there be a slam?'

'Are you forgetting the bidding?' asked Sister Benedict. 'I could hardly be any better for a strong two-bid. With anything more, I would have opened two clubs.'

By way of consolation, Sister Myrtle placed a Rowntree's fruit gum in her mouth. Blackcurrant was her favorite flavor — just what she needed at a stressful moment like this. There were only eleven tricks visible, with no apparent chance of a twelfth. Ah well, she would have to cash her winners and hope that someone unguarded the clubs.

Sister Myrtle won the diamond lead in her hand and continued with six rounds of spades, followed by the ♢A. These cards remained:

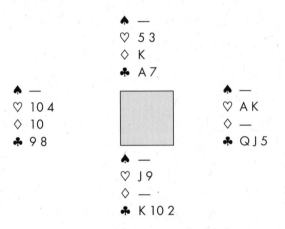

When the ♢K was led, Sister Thomas had an awkward discard in the East seat. She sucked in air between her remaining teeth. What should she throw? Hoping that her partner could provide some assistance in clubs, she eventually discarded the ♣5. Sister Myrtle discarded the ♡9 and continued with the ♣A and ♣K. The ♣Q and ♣J appeared on her right and, as if by a miracle, the ♣10 was good for a twelfth trick. The slam had been made.

Sister Benedict clapped her hands excitedly. 'I knew it was right to bid the slam in notrump,' she exclaimed. 'Sister Thomas would be sure to lead a heart against six spades and I'd have no chance at all, then!'

47. BROTHER CAMERON'S BREAKTHROUGH

'Evening, Abbot,' said Brother Cameron, flopping into the South seat.

The Abbot surveyed the disrespectful novice wearily. If his father hadn't made such a substantial donation to the St. Titus manuscript library, there was no way that he would tolerate such an attitude. Why the novice should speak in shorthand, rather than forming normal sentences, was a complete mystery.

'Doing well?' asked Brother Cameron.

Only three syllables that time, noted the Abbot. Each sentence is shorter than the previous one. 'If you are asking about the success of our session tonight,' he replied, 'then, yes, we are doing quite well. No doubt you're doing well yourselves or you wouldn't have asked.'

'No way,' muttered Brother Cameron.

'Lucius took a big penalty off us on the last round,' added Brother Damien

Typical, thought the Abbot. They hand Brother Lucius some undeserved huge score and now they will probably play above themselves. The players drew their cards for this board:

```
                 ♠ 9 6 4
                 ♡ K 7 6 3
                 ◇ 7 5
                 ♣ 8 7 4 2
♠ Q 10 5 3 2                        ♠ J 8
♡ 10 9 8 4     Neither Vul.        ♡ J 5 2
◇ 6 3          Dealer S            ◇ 10 9 4 2
♣ J 3                              ♣ Q 10 9 5
                 ♠ A K 7
                 ♡ A Q
                 ◇ A K Q J 8
                 ♣ A K 6
```

West	North	East	South
The	Brother	Brother	Brother
Abbot	Damien	Xavier	Cameron
			2♣
pass	2◇	pass	3◇
pass	3♡	pass	6NT
all pass			

Brother Cameron won the heart lead with the ace. Unless diamonds broke very badly, he had eleven top tricks. If clubs were 3-3, he could set up a long club in dummy as a twelfth trick and reach it by overtaking the ♡Q.

Unwilling to play for this chance immediately, Brother Cameron decided to run the diamonds. The Abbot discarded a spade, a club and then a heart; Brother Xavier released a club. The ♣A was cashed next, leaving these cards still out:

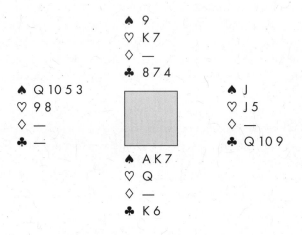

The Abbot was reluctant to throw another spade on the ♣K. If he did, declarer could unblock the ♡Q and put him on lead with ace, king and another spade, forcing him to lead to dummy's ♡K. His mind made up, the Abbot threw the ♡8.

Disappointed that the clubs were not breaking 3-3, Brother Cameron next cashed his two top spades. On the second round East had to find a discard. If he too discarded a heart, declarer would be able to overtake the ♡Q and score dummy's ♡7 for his twelfth trick. He therefore threw the ♣10 instead.

Brother Cameron smiled to himself. What an unusual hand! He cashed the ♡Q and exited with a club to East's bare ♣Q. Brother Xavier returned the ♡J, his last card, to dummy's ♡K and the slam had been made.

'That was a double steppingstone squeeze,' Brother Cameron announced proudly.

'A whole sentence, including a verb,' exclaimed the Abbot. 'Did you hear that, Xavier? Most youngsters manage their first full sentence well before the age of 19. Still, better late than never!'

48. THE HEADMASTER'S BRILLIANCY

'Ah, Matron, good to see you,' exclaimed the Headmaster. 'Are you and Madame Baguette carrying all before you tonight?'

'We were at one stage,' the Matron replied. 'On the first deal we bid to a very thin 3NT contract, with only the minimum point-count of 25 between us.'

The Headmaster had made up his mind to be pleasant to everyone on this occasion. 'Did you manage to make it?' he enquired.

The Matron beamed. 'I made an overtrick,' she replied. 'That can't happen very often with a minimum point-count.'

No indeed, thought the Headmaster. Not with the Matron playing the contract, anyway. The players drew their cards for this board:

```
                    ♠ Q 3
                    ♡ K 10 2
                    ◇ A Q 10 9 7 3
                    ♣ J 7
  ♠ 10 6 4                          ♠ 9 8 7 5 2
  ♡ 8 3            Neither Vul.     ♡ 9 7 6 4
  ◇ K 8 6 2        Dealer S         ◇ 4
  ♣ K Q 10 3                        ♣ 9 8 4
                    ♠ A K J
                    ♡ A Q J 5
                    ◇ J 5
                    ♣ A 6 5 2
```

West	North	East	South
The	Reverend	Madame	The
Matron	Benson	Baguette	Headmaster
			2NT
pass	6NT	all pass	

The Headmaster arrived in 6NT and the Matron led the ♣K. 'What a strange bid!' she exclaimed when the dummy went down. 'How can you have a six-card suit and not bid it?'

'It's better to play in notrump at Pairs scoring,' the Reverend Benson explained. 'In any case, a response of 3◇ would have been a transfer.'

'Of course it would, Matron,' said Madame Baguette. 'We play transfers opposite 2NT ourselves, don't you remember?'

'You'd have to bid 3◇ and follow it with 4◇, to cancel the transfer,' continued the Matron. 'Ace-queen to six is a rebiddable suit.'

The Headmaster could hardly believe what he was hearing. What if any parent discovered that someone so foolish was in charge of their son's health? They would look for another school immediately.

The Headmaster won the club lead with the ace and, hoping for the best, led the ◊J. He was relieved to see the Matron pause to think when this card appeared on the table. She obviously held the ◊K and was trying to work out whether she should cover. Unless she was void in diamonds, of course, and was wondering what to discard.

The Matron eventually produced a low diamond and the Headmaster ran the jack successfully. If diamonds were 3-2 he would make an overtrick. Could he make the slam if the Matron had started with four diamonds? Ah yes, he could cash all his major-suit winners and put the Matron under pressure.

The Headmaster abandoned diamonds for the moment, playing four rounds of hearts. On the last round he threw a diamond from dummy, retaining the potentially useful ♣J. He continued with two winners in spades, leaving this position:

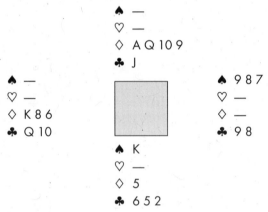

The Headmaster played his last spade and the Matron discarded the ♣10. 'Throw another diamond, Charlie,' he instructed.

When a diamond was played to the ten, East showed out and a triumphant gleam came to the Headmaster's eye. 'Play the jack of clubs,' he said.

The Matron won with the bare ♣Q and gave a small shake of the head. She had to lead from her ◊K8 into dummy's ◊AQ and the slam was made.

'Absolutely brilliant!' exclaimed the Headmaster. 'Totally inspired, there's no other way to describe it.'

Reverend Benson nodded happily. 'Thank you very much, Headmaster,' he replied. 'Had I been less inspired and bid the slam in diamonds, we'd have scored only 920 instead of 990.'

The Headmaster delivered a black glance. 'I was referring to my line of play,' he said. 'If I take a second diamond finesse early on, I would go down.'

The Reverend Benson was still basking in the unaccustomed compliment and heard not a word of this. 'They say that bridge is a bidders' game,' he continued. 'How very true that is!'

49. MRS. EL-DJEM'S CONTRIBUTION

A qualifying round of the Upper Bhumpopo National Pairs was about to start. Some thirty pairs had entered and the game was to take place in the open air, just outside the grain compound.

'150 mpengos each!' demanded Mjubu, as a group of ladies arrived.

'You mus' be jokin',' exclaimed Mrs. El-Djem, who was regaled in her usual finery. 'We ain't never paid for de bridge before.'

'Upper Bhumpopo Bridge Union makin' a charge of 100 mpengos for organizin' de event,' Mjubu replied. 'You gettin' three times de normal masterpoints too.'

'You sayin' 150, not 100,' said Mrs. El-Djem, tossing her head suspiciously and sending wafts of mango perfume into the air.

'Yeah, well, Witchdoctor makin' small surcharge,' explained Mjubu. 'Extra 50 is voluntary contribution, he say, but anyone refusin' to pay mos' probably regrettin' it.'

The other three ladies hastily handed over the 150 mpengos but Mrs. El-Djem was made of sterner stuff. She placed an orange 100-mpengo note on the table and moved defiantly to one of the stationary North-South positions.

The eighth round of the event saw the Witchdoctor arrive at Mrs. El-Djem's table. Although he and Mbozi were certain to qualify, the Witchdoctor had a personal score to settle with Mrs. El-Djem.

This was the first board of the round:

```
                  ♠ A Q 6
                  ♡ A K 8
                  ◇ A J 6 5
                  ♣ 7 3 2
  ♠ 10 5 4 2                   ♠ J 8 3
  ♡ 10 2         EW Vul.       ♡ 9 6 5 3
  ◇ 4            Dealer E      ◇ K 10 8 3
  ♣ Q J 10 9 5 4               ♣ 8 6
                  ♠ K 9 7
                  ♡ Q J 7 4
                  ◇ Q 9 7 2
                  ♣ A K
```

West	North	East	South
Witch-doctor	Mrs. Bakshee	Mbozi	Mrs. El-Djem
		pass	1NT
pass	6NT	all pass	

The Witchdoctor led the ♣Q against 6NT and Mrs. El-Djem won with the ♣A. She nodded her head approvingly as she surveyed the dummy. There were nine top tricks outside the diamond suit. Add three diamond tricks to the total and the slam would be hers.

At Trick 2 Mrs. El-Djem played a diamond to the jack. The finesse proved successful, Mbozi following with the ◊8 in the East seat.

'What was dat card you playin'?' queried Mrs. El-Djem.

In his usual sullen manner, Mbozi faced his ◊8.

Mrs. El-Djem paused to reassess the position in the diamond suit. If East had begun with ◊108 doubleton, she could pick up the suit without loss by leading the ◊Q on the second round. Whether or not West chose to cover with the ◊K, East's ◊10 would be pinned and she would end with a precious overtrick. Even if the ◊8 was a singleton, the slam would still be safe. After the ◊Q had been covered by the king and ace, her ◊97 would be good for an extra trick against the ◊10.

Mrs. El-Djem looked reprovingly at Mbozi. 'You mos' probably hopin' I didn't seein' de diamond eight,' she said. 'My nickname should be Eagle-eyes!'

Mrs. El-Djem returned to her hand with the ♠K and led the ◊Q from her hand. She could not believe it when the Witchdoctor showed out, discarding a club. It was no longer possible to score three diamond tricks and the slam went one down.

The Witchdoctor cackled with laughter. 'Mos' excellent play, Mbozi!' he cried. 'If you winnin' first round with de king, she pickin' up de diamonds for sure.'

Mbozi nodded happily. 'Workin' every time, dat one,' he observed.

Mrs. El-Djem was looking for revenge as the next board was placed on the table:

```
                 ♠ 9 5
                 ♡ 7 6 4 2
                 ◊ K J 9 2
                 ♣ Q 6 2
 ♠ K Q J 8 4 3            ♠ 10 6 2
 ♡ J 10 3                 ♡ K 9 5
 ◊ 10 8 5      Both Vul.  ◊ 7 6 4
 ♣ 5           Dealer S   ♣ 9 7 4 3
                 ♠ A 7
                 ♡ A Q 8
                 ◊ A Q 3
                 ♣ A K J 10 8
```

West	North	East	South
Witch-doctor	Mrs. Bakshee	Mbozi	Mrs. El-Djem
			2♣
2♠	pass	pass	3♣
pass	3◊	pass	3NT
pass	6NT	all pass	

The Witchdoctor led the ♠K against 6NT and Mrs. El-Djem watched anxiously as the dummy was laid out. The four-card diamond suit was a disappointment. It seemed that the slam might depend on a successful finesse in hearts.

The Witchdoctor's bid suggested that the ♡K was offside. Anyway, the first move must be to run the minor suits. Mrs. El-Djem cashed her clubs, throwing two hearts from dummy. She then started on the diamonds, reaching this position:

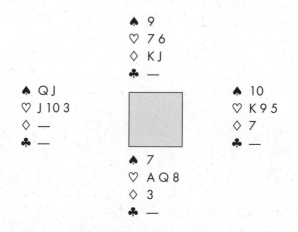

The Witchdoctor, sitting West, had foreseen the end position at an early stage. On the third round of diamonds he discarded the ♡10. When dummy's last diamond was played, East and the declarer both threw spades. The Witchdoctor surveyed his remaining cards gloomily, eventually parting with the ♡J.

Mrs. El-Djem could sense victory. It was entirely obvious that the Witchdoctor's last four cards had been the ♠QJ and ♡KJ. Realizing that he would be endplayed if he threw a spade, he had bared the ♡K. Mrs. El-Djem chuckled to herself. Fat lot of good that would do him!

Savoring the moment, Mrs. El-Djem led a heart from dummy. 'Now let me see, I got de ace-queen of hearts here,' she said, turning towards the Witchdoctor. 'What you think I should do? Finesse de queen?'

The Witchdoctor returned her gaze and gave a noncommittal sniff.

'Your last three cards are de ♠QJ and one heart,' continued Mrs. El-Djem remorselessly. 'You already thrown ten and jack of hearts. Let's takin' a look at your last heart!' With a vicious motion of the wrist she slapped the ♡A onto the table.

'My pleasure to show you de last heart,' exclaimed the Witchdoctor. With a triumphant cackle he spun the ♡3 onto the table. Mrs. El-Djem had to surrender the last two tricks to East's ♡K-9 and she was one down.'

'Serves you right for not makin' 50 mpengo contribution to charity,' declared the Witchdoctor. 'Anyway, you better payin' up pretty quick or your husband mos' probably hear somethin' tasty about what his wife do during de day.'

'Don' be ridiculous,' Mrs. El-Djem replied. 'I gotta clear conscience. My husband and me don' keepin' no secrets from each other.'

The Witchdoctor leaned towards her and whispered in her ear. 'In dat case he mus' knowin' about knife sharpener from Brazugah Village,' he said.

Maintaining her dignity, Mrs. El-Djem reached for her handbag. 'Well, if you sure it's for charity,' she said. 'I suppose I might makin' a small contribution.'

Quiz 25 *How would you play 6NT?*

```
              ♠ A Q 5
              ♡ Q 7
              ◇ A Q 7 6
              ♣ K J 10 4
♡10 led       ▭▭▭▭
              ♠ K 9
              ♡ K 5 2
              ◇ K 10 9 5
              ♣ A Q 7 2
```

West	North	East	South
			1NT
pass	6NT	all pass	

What is your plan when West leads the ♡10? **(The answer is on page 145.)**

50. BROTHER AELRED'S STRANGE FINESSE

'Visiting the St Hilda's Convent must have been a very pleasant rest for you, Abbot,' said Brother Aelred, easing himself into the South seat. 'I've been so busy over the last few days, I wouldn't have minded a nice holiday myself.'

'It wasn't a holiday,' retorted the Abbot. 'It club a pastoral visit. The nuns at St Hilda's found my time with them very beneficial spiritually. I received a letter from the Mother Superior only this morning, expressing their thanks.'

'Is that the letter you were reading at breakfast?' continued Brother Aelred. 'You know, the one with some bridge hands in it? You were trying to explain to me how she had managed to make six hearts with the trumps breaking 4-0.'

'Yes, I did manage to help them with their bridge too,' replied the Abbot. 'Several of the nuns mentioned how much their game had improved.'

This was the deal before them:

```
                    ♠ A J 9
                    ♡ K 8 6 2
                    ◇ K 8 4 3
                    ♣ Q 7
  ♠ 8 4 3                          ♠ 10 7 6 5
  ♡ J 10 9 7 5    Neither Vul.     ♡ 4 3
  ◇ 9 7 2          Dealer S        ◇ Q J 10 6
  ♣ J 3                            ♣ K 10 6
                    ♠ K Q 2
                    ♡ A Q
                    ◇ A 5
                    ♣ A 9 8 5 4 2
```

West	North	East	South
The	Brother	Brother	Brother
Abbot	Michael	Xavier	Aelred
			2NT
pass	6NT	all pass	

The Abbot led the ♡J and Brother Michael laid out his dummy, nodding happily. 'It just shows how wrong it is to look for a 4-4 fit,' he said. 'The Abbot would never have led one of my long suits if I'd given my hand away.'

'I quite agree. Well bid, partner,' Brother Aelred replied. 'Play low, will you?' He won in his hand with the ♡A and led a low club towards dummy. When the ♣3 appeared on the left, he paused for a moment. 'Seven, please,' he said.

East won with the ♣10 and returned a heart. Brother Aelred won in his hand with the queen, crossed to the ♠J and led the ♣Q. This was covered by the king and ace, the jack falling from West.

'Oh, that's very pretty,' declared Brother Michael. 'Did you see, partner? The four top honors, all on one trick.'

'Will you be quiet!' demanded the Abbot. 'Dummy is not allowed to participate in the proceedings. He should be seen and not heard.'

'They're all there now,' said Brother Aelred, displaying his remaining cards. 'Five club tricks are more than enough.'

The Abbot gazed at declarer's hand in disbelief. 'Your play in the club suit was way against the odds!' he exclaimed. 'It wins against Jx or 10x in my hand and loses to Kx, KJx, K10x and Kxx.'

'That's not right,' Brother Aelred replied. 'With a doubleton king, you would go in with the king. Even with three cards to the king, you would probably play the king. Otherwise you might get endplayed.'

'I've never heard such nonsense!' thundered the Abbot. 'You think that a top-class defender such as myself would give the position away by rising with the king from king-doubleton? Do you live in some kind of fantasy land?'

'I think he's right, Abbot,' said Brother Xavier. 'Most defenders would play the king, or at least think about it. When you get an unconsidered low card, finessing the seven has a lot going for it. I believe they call it an intra-finesse.'

'I'm surrounded by idiots,' exclaimed the Abbot. He turned to glare at Brother Michael. 'There's no need to carry your non-participation as dummy to extremes. You haven't filled in the score sheet, have you?'

Quiz 26 *How would you play 6NT?*

<pre>
                    ♠ A K
                    ♡ A Q 6
                    ♢ A 8 7 5
                    ♣ K 8 4 3
    ♣10 led   ▭▭▭▭▭▭▭
                    ♠ 8 5 4
                    ♡ J 3 2
                    ♢ K 2
                    ♣ A Q J 7 5
</pre>

West	North	East	South
		3◊	pass
pass	dbl	pass	3NT
pass	4NT	pass	6NT
all pass			

How will you play 6NT when the ♣10 is led? (**The answer is on page 150.**)

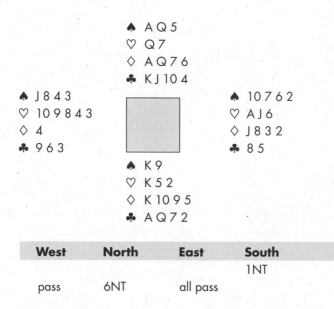

♠ A Q 5
♡ Q 7
◊ A Q 7 6
♣ K J 10 4

♠ J 8 4 3
♡ 10 9 8 4 3
◊ 4
♣ 9 6 3

♠ 10 7 6 2
♡ A J 6
◊ J 8 3 2
♣ 8 5

♠ K 9
♡ K 5 2
◊ K 10 9 5
♣ A Q 7 2

West	North	East	South
			1NT
pass	6NT	all pass	

West leads the ♡10 and you see that you have eleven certain tricks, counting one in hearts. A twelfth trick will come from the diamonds, provided they break 3-2 or you can guess which defender holds ◊Jxxx. On many such deals you would simply play off your winners in the other suits, which might provide some clue as to which defender was likely to be longer in diamonds. Three rounds of spades and four rounds of clubs will not help you particularly here, because West will show up with seven black cards to East's six. Not much in it. How else can you approach the problem?

Consider the lie of the heart suit first. It is well nigh impossible that West has led from the ♡A, so East must hold this card. You play low from dummy at Trick 1. If East plays his ace on thin air you will have two heart tricks, enough for the contract. Let's assume that East plays low and you win with the king. What now?

You should continue with the ◊A and ◊K. If the diamonds prove to be 3-2, the contract is yours. If East shows up with only one diamond, you can run the ◊10 for the contract.

What happens when the cards lie as in the diagram and West shows out on the second diamond? You have a guaranteed throw in against East and no guess of any sort will be required. You cash your seven winners in the black suits, throwing a heart from the South hand. East has to retain the ♡A and ◊J8, to avoid handing you a twelfth trick directly. You exit with the ♡Q to his bare ace and at Trick 12 he has to lead away from the ◊J. You score the ◊10 and ◊Q separately and the slam is yours.

51. BECKIE'S GOOD JUDGMENT

Every Tuesday afternoon there was a ladies bridge four and today it was the turn of Miriam to host the gathering.

Judith looked down at her watch. 'Beckie is not here yet?' she said. 'She thinks perhaps that two o'clock means half-past two?'

'She had a hair appointment this morning,' Miriam replied. 'Such a lot she needs doing to it, as you know, and those girls at Blumberg's are so lazy. They maybe overran the time.'

The doorbell rang and Miriam rose to open the front door. 'Ah, Beckie, a new style they gave you!' she exclaimed. 'Much more suitable, at your age. Come, show the girls; I am sure they will like it.'

Admiration of the new hairstyle and exchange of the latest news did not take long and it was less than an hour later when the first hand was dealt:

```
                    ♠ A Q J 10 3
                    ♡ K 4
                    ◇ 6 3
                    ♣ K 10 6 4
    ♠ 9 8 7 5                       ♠ 6 2
    ♡ Q 10 9 2    ┌───────────┐     ♡ 8 6 5 3
    ◇ Q 9 5 4     │Neither Vul.│    ◇ 10 7 2
    ♣ 3           │  Dealer S  │     ♣ Q J 9 8
                  └───────────┘
                    ♠ K 4
                    ♡ A J 7
                    ◇ A K J 8
                    ♣ A 7 5 2
```

West	North	East	South
Judith	Beckie	Rachel	Miriam
			2NT
pass	3♡	pass	3♠
pass	6NT	all pass	

Beckie showed her spades with a transfer response and then seemed at a loss for what to do next. Eventually she closed the auction with a leap to 6NT. Judith led the ♠9 and down went the dummy.

'What is this bidding?' exclaimed Judith. 'Six notrump, you say? You might have a spade fit; you might have a club fit. Over Miriam's three spades, you must bid four clubs. That is how it should be bid.'

'It was very awkward,' Beckie observed. 'It had to be a slam, of course, and when there is a notrump opening I like to play four clubs as Gerber.'

Judith raised her eyebrows. Did anyone still use Gerber nowadays? 'Michael and I play something more complicated,' she said. 'We can find all the fits, believe me.'

Miriam won the spade lead with the king and saw that she had eleven top tricks. There would be time later to finesse in one of the red suits, if necessary. The first task was to seek an extra trick from the club suit. She would lead ace and another club, covering West's card. Unless West happened to show out on the second round, that would guarantee three club tricks.

Everyone followed to the ♣A but West did indeed show out on the second round of clubs, throwing a spade. Miriam won the trick with dummy's ♣K and paused to reassess the position. Ah, of course, now she had a certain endplay on Judith. Sometimes bridge could be such a pleasant pastime!

Miriam cashed three more rounds of spades, throwing the two club losers from her hand. This position had been reached:

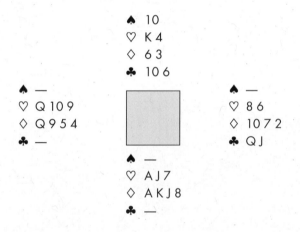

Savoring the moment, Miriam led a low diamond from dummy, inserting the eight from her hand. Judith won the trick cheaply, with the nine, but then had to lead into one of declarer's red-suit tenaces. Miriam had her slam.

'Such a nice play, you made there,' said Beckie, who had made little attempt to follow what was going on. 'I had a feeling 6NT would be best.'

Miriam turned towards Judith, her great rival. 'You would have looked for a club fit, Judith?' she asked. 'In six clubs, with this break, there is no chance at all.'

'No harm in showing what you have,' Judith replied. 'Slam bidding is a question of judgment, that is what I told Michael the other day. On this particular deal we would probably have ended in 6NT, you are right.'

Miriam could have no complaints at the hands she was being dealt. A couple of deals later, she found herself sorting through a 21-count. This was the layout:

```
              ♠ Q 7 6
              ♥ Q J 4 3
              ◇ 7 6 4
              ♣ A Q 5
♠ A J 10 9 5 4 2                    ♠ 3
♥ 8            ┌─────────┐          ♥ 10 7 6 5 2
◇ J 9 3        │ NS Vul. │          ◇ Q 10 2
♣ 10 9         │ Dealer W│          ♣ 8 7 4 3
               └─────────┘
              ♠ K 8
              ♥ A K 9
              ◇ A K 8 5
              ♣ K J 6 2
```

West	North	East	South
Judith	Beckie	Rachel	Miriam
3♠	pass	pass	3NT
pass	6NT	all pass	

Judith led the ♣10 against 6NT and peered disapprovingly at the dummy that went down. 'Only 11 points you have, Beckie?' she said. 'You don't think your partner might perhaps bid 3NT on 17 or 18 points?'

'It was awkward to bid,' Beckie replied. 'With my normal partners I would make a Gerber slam-try, as I mentioned before. Good players like you and Miriam don't like that bid, I realize.'

Miriam won the club lead in dummy, crossed to her hand with the ♥A and led the ♠8. Judith could not afford to go in with the ace, giving declarer two spade tricks, and dummy's ♠Q won the trick. Miriam had eleven top tricks now and would need to develop one extra trick from the diamond suit. She gave a small shrug of the shoulders. Diamonds would have to be 3-3 and, yes, she would need to find East with the ◇Q. Otherwise Judith would gain the lead and be able to cash some spade tricks.

Miriam led a low diamond from dummy, winning with the ace when a low card appeared on her right. She returned to dummy with the remaining club honor and led another diamond towards her hand. It would do East no good to rise with the ◇Q because declarer would allow that card to win, leaving the safe hand on lead. East followed with the ◇10 and South's ◇K won the trick.

When Miriam exited with a third round of diamonds, she could not believe her good luck when Judith produced the ◇J and Rachel had to win with the ◇Q. As the bidding had suggested, East had no spade to return. Miriam won the club return and was then able to claim the contract.

'Only 11 points I held, but I had a feeling 6NT would be there,' Beckie declared. 'When you have played for as long as I have, you know in your bones what is the right bid.'

Rachel looked apologetically across the table. 'The queen of diamonds, I did not want,' she exclaimed. 'If you have that card, Judith, she is down.'

Judith nodded. 'Diamonds break 3-3 and you hold the queen,' she said. 'With the cards like that, there was nothing we could do.'

Miriam was looking as if she had just won the lottery. Two slams bid and made, in just twenty minutes, and both against Judith! Nothing could improve such a wonderful moment unless... wait a moment... could Judith not have beaten this contract?

'It was difficult for you, Judith,' said Miriam.

'Difficult?' Judith exclaimed. 'What do you mean?'

'You could not lead a diamond?' continued Miriam. 'Beckie plays her queen and I have no chance. I cannot duck or you will score a spade trick. If I win and lead towards the queen of spades, as before, I can no longer set up an extra diamond trick.'

'Miriam is right,' declared Rachel. 'Lead a diamond, partner, and I get rid of my queen at a safe moment.'

With a self-satisfied smile, Beckie gave her new hairstyle a congratulatory pat. 'I had a feeling Judith wouldn't lead a diamond,' she said.

Quiz 27 *How would you play 6NT?*

```
              ♠ A Q 6 2
              ♡ Q 10 5
              ◇ K 2
              ♣ A K J 2
♣10 led     [              ]
              ♠ 8 7 5 3
              ♡ A K 3
              ◇ A Q 6
              ♣ Q 7 3
```

West	North	East	South
	1♣	pass	1♠
pass	4♠	pass	6NT
all pass			

How will you play 6NT when West leads the ♣10? **(The answer is on page 151.)**

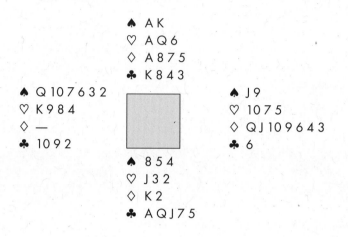

East opens 3◇ and West leads the ♣10 against your eventual contract of 6NT. You have ten tricks on top and a second heart trick will make it eleven. How can you conjure a twelfth trick?

If West holds six spades and the ♡K, you will be able to squeeze him in the majors. You play five rounds of clubs, throwing a diamond from dummy, and West discards two spades. A finesse of the ♡Q succeeds and you cash dummy's two spade honors. West throws a heart on the ◇A, leaving this position:

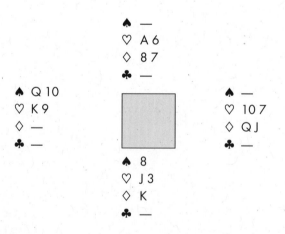

When you play a diamond to the king, West is caught in a strip squeeze. If he discards a spade, you will throw him with a spade to lead away from the ♡K. If instead he throws the ♡9, you can score the ♡A and ♡J. Since you need spades to be 6-2 for the squeeze to work, you will have no difficulty in reading which cards West has kept.

```
                    ♠ A Q 6 2
                    ♡ Q 10 5
                    ◇ K 2
                    ♣ A K J 2
    ♠ J 10 4                          ♠ K 9
    ♡ 7 2                             ♡ J 9 8 6 4
    ◇ J 8 5 3                         ◇ 10 9 7 4
    ♣ 10 9 8 5                        ♣ 6 4
                    ♠ 8 7 5 3
                    ♡ A K 3
                    ◇ A Q 6
                    ♣ Q 7 3
```

West	North	East	South
	1♣	pass	1♠
pass	4♠	pass	6NT
all pass			

How will you play 6NT when West leads the ♣10?

Perhaps you have been staring at this problem for a while, wondering what on earth the point can be. Three of the suits are solid and you need two tricks from the spade suit to give you the slam. A successful finesse of the ♠Q would suffice. You could increase your prospects marginally by cashing the ♠A on the first round, picking up a singleton ♠K offside, before leading towards the ♠Q. That would be a rather weak problem in an otherwise excellent book (ahem).

The best way to play the slam is to win the club lead with dummy's ♣A and to lead a low spade from dummy. Most of the world's East players will be caught unprepared when they hold a doubleton ♠K. They will either rise with the king or make it very clear that they are considering doing so. This will allow you to score the two spade tricks that you need.

I hope you don't still think that this is a lightweight problem and that no defender in your own game would play the ♠K from a doubleton holding. I remember losing a quarter-final match in a national knockout tournament because the other team's declarer attempted this ploy successfully and it did not occur to our own declarer.

Tony Forrester once pointed out in an excellent Bols Bridge Tip that you can often cause problems for the defender on your right by leading a low card toward the closed hand. This deal is a good example of what he had in mind.

52. THE ABBOT'S HOT STREAK

'Phew!' exclaimed Brother Cameron, flopping into the South seat. 'Hot in here.'

The Abbot glared at the novice. 'Are you forgetting our venerable founder, St. Titus?' he demanded.

Brother Cameron looked back uncomprehendingly.

The Abbot adopted a pious expression. 'The summer of 1549 was one of the hottest on record,' he continued, 'and yet St. Titus wore long woolen underwear and a double cassock every day of that year.'

Brother Cameron, not daring to show any reaction, reached for his cards.

'Such extreme discomfort and yet he never passed a single adverse comment on it,' declared the Abbot. 'A splendid example to us all.'

Play began and a few moments later the novices were in a slam:

```
                  ♠ 7 5
                  ♡ A Q J 10 4
                  ◇ A 8 7 3
                  ♣ J 6
♠ A Q 10 4 2                      ♠ J 9 8 3
♡ 9 8 2         Neither Vul.      ♡ 6 5 3
◇ J 9 6 5        Dealer N         ◇ 10 2
♣ 4                               ♣ Q 9 8 3
                  ♠ K 6
                  ♡ K 7
                  ◇ K Q 4
                  ♣ A K 10 7 5 2
```

West	North	East	South
The	Brother	Brother	Brother
Abbot	Damien	Xavier	Cameron
	1♡	pass	2♣
pass	2◇	pass	2♠
pass	3♡	pass	4NT
pass	5♠	pass	6NT
all pass			

Brother Cameron opted for Roman Keycard Blackwood at his third turn and was soon in 6NT. The Abbot led the ♡9 and declarer won with dummy's ♡10. 'Jack of clubs,' he said.

Brother Xavier covered with the queen and the young declarer won with the ace. When he cashed a second round of the suit, the Abbot discarded a spade. Brother Cameron paused to assess the situation. He had eleven certain tricks at his disposal. A 3-3 diamond break would bump this to twelve, as would a successful lead towards the ♠K. The latter option was not attractive because the Abbot's lead in dummy's main suit had suggested difficult holdings in the other three suits; it was therefore quite likely that he held the ♠A. Apart from that, the Abbot had hesitated momentarily after the fourth-suit bid in spades. Perhaps he had been considering a lead-directing double.

Since Brother Cameron was not planning to lead towards the ♠K, he saw that he had nothing to lose by cashing the ♣10. He then turned to the heart suit, soon reaching this position:

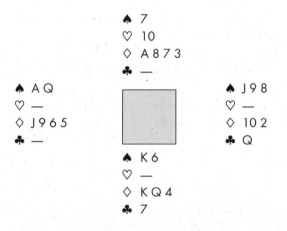

```
              ♠ 7
              ♡ 10
              ◇ A 8 7 3
              ♣ —
  ♠ A Q                      ♠ J 9 8
  ♡ —                        ♡ —
  ◇ J 9 6 5                  ◇ 10 2
  ♣ —                        ♣ Q
              ♠ K 6
              ♡ —
              ◇ K Q 4
              ♣ 7
```

Brother Cameron threw the ♣7 on dummy's last heart and turned to observe the Abbot's final discard. He had to wait quite a few moments. Eventually, the Abbot threw the ♠Q.

It was obvious how the cards lay. If the Abbot had been down to ♠AQJ and three diamonds, it would have been unethical to think for a while before throwing the ♠Q. The Abbot had many faults but being unethical was not one of them. Not in a meaningless pairs, anyway. Brother Cameron led the ♠7 from dummy and contributed the ♠6 from his hand. The bare ace appeared on his left, as he had expected, and he was able to claim the remaining tricks.

'Lucky guess at the end,' muttered the Abbot. 'Had I held AQ9 of spades and three diamonds, I would have made the same discard of the spade queen. Play a spade then and you would go down, even though the diamonds broke 3-3.'

Brother Cameron looked back impassively. 'Yes,' he said.

'Holding four diamonds, of course, I was robbed of the opportunity for a defensive brilliancy,' continued the Abbot. He shook his head sadly as he returned his cards to the wallet. 'Typical of our bad luck that diamonds didn't break 3-3.'

A round or two later, the Abbot and Brother Xavier faced the monastery's top pair, Brother Lucius and Brother Paulo. This was the first board that they played:

                    ♠ A J 7
                    ♡ A 4
                    ◇ Q J 10 4
                    ♣ K 10 9 3

♠ 10   ♠ Q 9 8 6 4 2
♡ Q 9 7 5 3   **NS Vul.**   ♡ K 10 8
◇ 9 8 5 3   **Dealer E**   ◇ 7 2
♣ 8 6 4   ♣ J 5

                    ♠ K 5 3
                    ♡ J 6 2
                    ◇ A K 6
                    ♣ A Q 7 2

West	North	East	South
Brother	Brother	The	Brother
Xavier	Paulo	Abbot	Lucius
		2♠	2NT
pass	6NT	all pass	

Brother Paulo took a typically optimistic view of his hand, raising directly to 6NT. West led the ♠10 and Brother Lucius paused to consider his best line. It seemed that the best chance was to cash the minor suits, aiming to endplay East. Yes, if the Abbot held the ♡K and ♡Q, he would have no escape.

Lucius cashed four rounds of clubs, the Abbot discarding two spades. He continued with four rounds of diamonds and the Abbot threw one more spade followed by the ♡8. These cards remained:

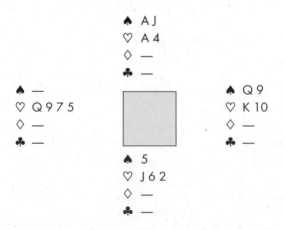

                    ♠ A J
                    ♡ A 4
                    ◇ —
                    ♣ —

♠ —   ♠ Q 9
♡ Q 9 7 5   ♡ K 10
◇ —   ◇ —
♣ —   ♣ —

                    ♠ 5
                    ♡ J 6 2
                    ◇ —
                    ♣ —

When Lucius called for the ♡A the Abbot could visualize his fate if he retained the king. Praying that declarer would not hold the queen of the suit, he ditched his king under the ace. 'Small heart, please,' said Brother Lucius.

The ♡10 appeared from East and Brother Lucius underplayed with the ♡6. The defenders were powerless. If West overtook the ♡10 with the ♡Q, this would set up the ♡J in declarer's hand; he would then have to return a heart, allowing declarer to score that card. Brother Xavier chose instead to play low on the trick but the Abbot then had to lead into the dummy's spade tenace. Declarer had lost only one trick, to the ♡10, and the slam had been made.

Brother Xavier gave the Abbot a good-natured smile. 'Difficult for you,' he said. 'You have to discard the ♡10, don't you, coming down to ♡K8? Then, when you unblock the king, the way is clear for me to overtake your eight on the second round.'

There was a brief pause while the Abbot digested this unwelcome information. 'I realized it the moment I let the eight go,' he replied. 'It's so incredibly hot in here, it's difficult to think straight.'

'That reminds me of a story about our blessed founder, St. Titus,' said Brother Lucius. 'Apparently, 1549 was one of the hottest summers ever witnessed and...'

'I think we're all aware of that one,' intervened the Abbot. 'Instead of telling stories that we've all heard before, perhaps you could exert your strength on that window behind you. Surely it must open wider than that!'

Quiz 28 *How would you play 6NT?*

```
               ♠ K 10 3
               ♡ K 8 2
               ◇ A 10 5 2
               ♣ K 7 5
  ♣10 led      ┌──────────┐
               ♠ A 5 2
               ♡ A 7
               ◇ K Q 8 7 3
               ♣ A Q J
```

West	North	East	South
			2NT
pass	6NT	all pass	

How will you play 6NT when West leads the ♣10? **(The answer is on page 158.)**

53. FRIAR TUCK'S PRIORITIES

It was a sunny morning in Sherwood Forest and the ten o'clock archery practice had just finished. Four of the outlaws were sitting cross-legged under the shade of a giant oak tree, enjoying a game of bridge.

'Taking your lunch already, Tuck?' queried Robin Hood.

'Just a mid-morning snack,' Friar Tuck replied. 'Shame to waste these honey cakes. They don't keep fresh for long.'

Little John shook his head disapprovingly. 'If you get honey on these cards you can pay for a new pack yourself,' he said. 'They're not cheap, you know.'

Friar Tuck laughed. 'When was the last time you ever paid for anything?' he asked. 'I happen to know that these cards were part of the spoils from last week's raid on a house in Nottingham. You know, the place where Lord Leysdale keeps that mistress of his.'

'Might have been,' Little John replied. 'No point makin' the cards all sticky, anyway.'

Friar Tuck savored his last mouthful of honey cake, sucked his fingers clean and proceeded to deal this hand:

```
                    ♠ K 8 2
                    ♡ Q 10 7 2
                    ◇ Q 8 2
                    ♣ A Q 8
    ♠ Q 9 4                          ♠ J 10 6 3
    ♡ 6 3          Neither Vul.      ♡ 9 8 5
    ◇ 9 6 4        Dealer S          ◇ 10 7 5
    ♣ J 10 9 4 3                      ♣ K 7 2
                    ♠ A 7 5
                    ♡ A K J 4
                    ◇ A K J 3
                    ♣ 6 5
```

West	North	East	South
Robin	Will	Little	Friar
Hood	Scarlet	John	Tuck
			2NT
pass	6NT	all pass	

Robin Hood led the ♣J and down went the dummy. Friar Tuck surveyed it with no great affection. Why in Heaven's name hadn't Will used the Bishop of Carlisle's new 3♣ convention to seek a 4-4 heart fit? Playing in 6♡, he could have ruffed a club in his hand for a twelfth trick.

Even such a bold player as Robin Hood would not lead from a KJ10 combination against 6NT, particularly when the hand on his right had opened 2NT. No, East must hold the ♣K and in that case making the slam was going to be difficult. Suppose he ducked the opening lead and rose with the ♣A on the second round. He would then succeed when East's ♣K was doubleton, or when East held the sole guard in the spades and could be squeezed in the black suits.

Friar Tuck could see a better line. He rose with the ♣A at Trick 1 and ran his winners in the red suits. This was the end position that he reached:

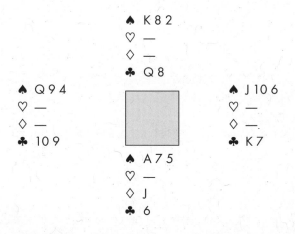

```
              ♠ K 8 2
              ♡ —
              ♢ —
              ♣ Q 8

♠ Q 9 4                        ♠ J 10 6
♡ —                            ♡ —
♢ —                            ♢ —
♣ 10 9                         ♣ K 7

              ♠ A 7 5
              ♡ —
              ♢ J
              ♣ 6
```

Robin Hood could not afford to throw the ♣10 or ♣9 on the last diamond, since declarer could then lead the ♣Q, pinning West's remaining club and establishing the ♣8 as his twelfth trick. He discarded a spade instead and a spade was thrown from dummy. Little John was then faced with the same dilemma as his partner. If he threw the ♣7, declarer would be able to duck a club, setting up dummy's ♣Q. He eventually threw a spade, as his partner had done, and Friar Tuck then scored three spade tricks for the contract.

Will Scarlet nodded approvingly. 'Nicely played, Tuck,' he declared. 'They do say that honey is good for the brain!'

Two outlaws came running into the forest glade. 'Armed soldiers approaching on the north-east path,' one of them cried. 'Prepare yourselves!'

Robin Hood leapt to his feet. 'Fetch your bows, lads!' he cried. 'Let's give the Sheriff's men the welcome that is their due.'

'Wait a minute, we haven't settled up yet,' protested Friar Tuck. 'Now, what's the bonus for the first game of an unfinished rubber?'

ANSWER TO **QUIZ 28** (*page 155*)

```
                    ♠ K 10 3
                    ♡ K 8 2
                    ◇ A 10 5 2
                    ♣ K 7 5
   ♠ J 8 7 6 4                        ♠ Q 9
   ♡ J 9 6 3                          ♡ Q 10 5 4
   ◇ —                                ◇ J 9 6 4
   ♣ 10 9 8 6                         ♣ 4 3 2
                    ♠ A 5 2
                    ♡ A 7
                    ◇ K Q 8 7 3
                    ♣ A Q J
```

West	North	East	South
			2NT
pass	6NT	all pass	

How would you play 6NT when West leads the ♣10?

The original declarer took only ten seconds over the play, which proved inadequate. He won the club lead with the ace and played the ◇K. 'Can you believe it?' he exclaimed, when West showed out. There was no way to recover and he went one down.

Declarer failed to notice that he could pick up a 4-0 diamond break on either side, provided he guessed which defender was likely to have the four-card length.

Before making the key decision in diamonds, you should take a look at the other three suits. The defender who is shorter in those suits is likely to be longer in diamonds. To this end, the best move at Trick 2 is a spade to dummy's ten. East wins with the queen and you capture his return. You can then cash your remaining winners in the black suits. Both defenders follow to three clubs and you discover that West has five spades to East's two. Rather surprisingly, you may think, this makes it ten times more likely that East, rather than West, will hold four diamonds (10% compared with 1%). You cash the ◇A and can then pick up East's diamond holding with a repeated finesse in the suit. The ♡K will be the entry for the second diamond finesse.

54. BROTHER CAMERON'S OBVIOUS BID

The Abbot connected to the website at *www.ecatsbridge.com* and clicked to see the results from the Hursley Village heat of the charity pairs. There they were: 649th A. Yorke-Smith & B. Xavier 52.94%. How on earth could they have done so badly? It had been quite an effort to persuade the Hursley woman to let them play at their club, too. You'd expect such moderate players to welcome a renowned expert in their midst. Would a 24-handicap golfer not give his right arm to play a couple of holes against Tiger Woods?

The Abbot made his way to the senior cardroom and took his seat opposite Brother Xavier at Table 5. Ah well, back to the usual Thursday pairs at the monastery. With masterpoints at an uninflated non-charity level, they would doubtless achieve a record score.

The first round of the evening brought Brother Aelred to the table. 'Get the worst over first,' he muttered, as he took his seat.

The Abbot surveyed his opponent uncertainly. 'What on earth do you mean?' he demanded.

'No offence intended, Abbot,' Brother Aelred replied. 'You usually do rather well against us. That's all.'

So does every pair in the monastery, thought the Abbot. Not that there was any point in pursuing the matter.

This was the first board of the round:

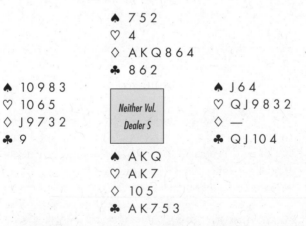

West	North	East	South
Brother	*Brother*	*Brother*	*The*
Aelred	*Xavier*	*Michael*	*Abbot*
			2♣
pass	3◇	pass	3NT
pass	6NT	all pass	

Brother Aelred led the ♠10 against 6NT and surveyed Brother Xavier's dummy with a puzzled expression. 'You don't play four clubs as Gerber in that auction?' he asked.

'I didn't bid four clubs,' replied Brother Xavier. 'I raised 3NT to 6NT.'

'Play low,' said the Abbot.

'It's rather unusual bidding a slam without asking for aces, isn't it?' persisted Brother Aelred. 'When the Abbot bid 3NT, I would have bid four clubs on your hand.'

'I said play low,' repeated the Abbot. 'If there's any time left at the end of the round, you can conduct an inquest into our bidding then.'

The Abbot won the first trick with the ♠A and led the ◇10. Brother Aelred covered with the jack and the Abbot paused for thought. Making 6NT, with or without an overtrick, would be a huge pairs score in this modest field. It must surely be right to take the safety play, guarding against a 4-1 diamond break. 'Play low,' he said.

When East showed out, the Abbot laughed openly. He turned towards Brother Aelred. 'You covered from jack-nine to five?' he exclaimed. 'I can hardly believe it.'

The Abbot won the spade continuation and took the marked finesse of dummy's ◇8, proceeding to claim the contract.

'I had to cover the ten of diamonds with the jack,' Brother Aelred explained. 'If I play low, you can run the ten.'

'Yes, I was going to run the ten,' said the Abbot. 'But I only make four diamond tricks then, instead of five. You would have a stopper in the suit.'

Brother Xavier leaned forward. 'How do the clubs break?' he asked. 'If you run the diamond ten and East shows out, you can try to set up the clubs.'

Good point, thought the Abbot as he reached anxiously for Brother Aelred's curtain card. Excellent! He had only one club. The Great Shuffler did occasionally ensure that justice was done. 'The clubs are 4-1,' he announced. 'It should be a top for us.'

Brother Aelred turned towards Brother Xavier. 'Diamonds was my best suit too,' he said. 'If you hadn't bid diamonds, I would have led a diamond.'

'Just as well you didn't,' observed the Abbot, writing down the score in his card. 'A low diamond lead leaves me with no chance!'

A few rounds later, the Abbot faced his least favorite opponent, Brother Cameron.

'Any good hands in the Charity, Abbot?' asked the novice, as he flopped into the South chair.

The Abbot pretended not to hear. How on earth did Brother Cameron know that he had played in the Charity? No doubt he had already viewed the results on the Internet, passing on the amusing details to the entire novitiate. He could just imagine the scene. 'The Abbot was playing down in the Village last Tuesday. Guess where he came in the national ranking list?'

This was the first deal of the round:

```
              ♠ A 7 3
              ♡ A 9 5
              ◇ K Q 5 4
              ♣ K 6 5
♠ —                          ♠ J 9 8 6 2
♡ Q J 10 8 7 6 4   Both Vul.  ♡ 2
◇ 10 9 2          Dealer W   ◇ 7 6 3
♣ A J 3                      ♣ 10 9 8 4
              ♠ K Q 10 5 4
              ♡ K 3
              ◇ A J 8
              ♣ Q 7 2
```

West	North	East	South
The	Brother	Brother	Brother
Abbot	Damien	Xavier	Cameron
4♡	dbl	pass	6NT
all pass			

The Abbot opened at the four-level, hoping to create a problem for the two novices. A few seconds later he found himself leading the ♡Q against 6NT.

Brother Cameron won the first trick with the ♡K and cashed the ♠K, discovering the 5-0 break. Just as well they weren't in six spades, he thought. Mind you, some pairs wouldn't be in a slam at all on those values.

At Trick 2 the novice led a club toward dummy. The Abbot had to play low, to avoid giving declarer two club tricks, and dummy's ♣K won the trick. Brother Cameron paused to consider his continuation. It seemed that he should be able to catch the Abbot in a squeeze without the count. Should he play spades first or diamonds? If he played the spade suit first, taking the marked finesse against East, he would have no good discard from dummy on the fourth round; he would have to throw one of the threat cards in hearts or clubs. Surely it must be right to play the diamonds first.

Brother Cameron played four rounds of diamonds, throwing a spade from the South hand. He then cashed the ♠A and finessed the ♠10. These cards remained:

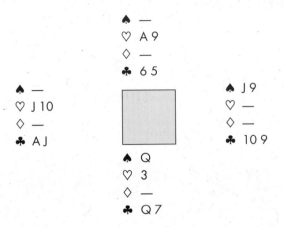

```
                    ♠ —
                    ♡ A 9
                    ◇ —
                    ♣ 6 5
  ♠ —                              ♠ J 9
  ♡ J 10        ┌─────────┐        ♡ —
  ◇ —           │         │        ◇ —
  ♣ A J         └─────────┘        ♣ 10 9
                    ♠ Q
                    ♡ 3
                    ◇ —
                    ♣ Q 7
```

When the ♠Q appeared on the table the Abbot had no good card to play. He eventually decided to part with the ♣J. 'Throw the nine of hearts,' instructed Brother Cameron. Declarer's ♣7 drew the bare ace from the Abbot and the slam was home. Brother Cameron nodded to himself. Yes, he had needed two clubs in dummy at the end. Had he cashed the spades before the diamonds, throwing a club from dummy, he would have gone down.

The Abbot gritted his teeth. 'Nothing we could do, partner,' he declared. 'Once they reach 6NT, the hand plays itself.'

'That's not a very generous assessment, Abbot,' Brother Xavier replied. 'I thought he played it very well.'

Brother Damien's eyes lit up as he inspected the score sheet. 'It's a top for us, partner,' he reported. 'Everyone else played in spades, quite a few of them at the game-level.'

The Abbot raised his eyes in disbelief. 'Why on earth should anyone play in spades?' he demanded. 'I don't know why I grace such a low standard game with my presence. In most bridge clubs, 6NT bid and made would be a flat board!'

55. THE PARROT'S BRILLIANT DEFENSE

Except during the two-month rainy season, the Bozwambi tribe played most of its bridge outdoors. Five tables had been set up in the shade provided by the cola trees and the Tuesday afternoon duplicate was in progress.

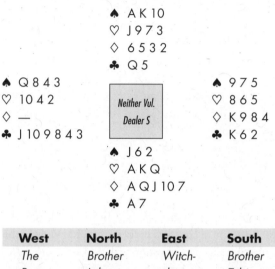

```
              ♠ A K 10
              ♡ J 9 7 3
              ◇ 6 5 3 2
              ♣ Q 5
♠ Q 8 4 3                      ♠ 9 7 5
♡ 10 4 2      Neither Vul.     ♡ 8 6 5
◇ —           Dealer S         ◇ K 9 8 4
♣ J 10 9 8 4 3                 ♣ K 6 2
              ♠ J 6 2
              ♡ A K Q
              ◇ A Q J 10 7
              ♣ A 7
```

West	North	East	South
The	Brother	Witch-	Brother
Parrot	Luke	doctor	Tobias
			2NT
pass	4NT	pass	6NT
all pass			

The Parrot leaned towards his teak-wood cardholder, extracted the ♣J with his beak and placed it carefully on the table. When the dummy appeared, he eyed Brother Luke disdainfully. 'Only 10 points, only 10 points!' he squawked.

'I must say, I rather agree with him,' Brother Tobias observed. 'My 2NT shows 20-22 points, so you need a bit more than 10 points to try for a slam.'

Brother Luke brushed a fly from his forearm. 'Nothing ventured, nothing gained,' he said. 'Anyway, playing in 3NT wouldn't be much fun for you.'

Brother Tobias had little sympathy for his partner's attitude. He would be happy enough trying to score three overtricks in 3NT. Why risk a complete bottom, going down in the slam? Now, what were his prospects? Five diamond tricks, four heart tricks and three top winners in the black suits would bring his total to twelve. A human player would not dream of leading away from a king against 6NT. Perhaps the Parrot had different ideas. 'Queen, please,' he said.

When the Witchdoctor covered with the ♣K, Brother Tobias won with the ♣A. He led the ♠2 to dummy's ♠A and a diamond to the queen then brought good news and bad news — the finesse won but the Parrot showed out, discarding a club. 'Having none?' exclaimed Brother Tobias. 'Are you sure?'

'No diamonds, no diamonds!' screeched the Parrot, glaring at Brother Tobias. It was very irritating to be treated as an idiot, just because you'd been born with wings instead of arms. Discrimination like that should be illegal.

Brother Tobias paused for further reflection. To take two more diamond finesses, he would need two further entries to dummy. Like it or not, he would have to steel himself to finesse the ♠10. If the finesse succeeded, he would have the extra entry that he needed. His mind made up, Brother Tobias cashed the three heart honors in his hand and then placed the ♠6 on the table.

The Parrot tilted his head to one side, a valuable aid to concentration. If declarer held the ♠J, he might intend to finesse dummy's ♠10 at this stage. This cunning plan had a flaw in it! The Parrot leaned towards his cardholder and flicked the ♠Q onto the table. Brother Tobias had to win with dummy's ♠K. Since his ♠J would now win the third round of the suit, he was in dummy for the last time. He cashed the ♡J, throwing his club loser, and took a second diamond finesse. He then cut his losses by cashing the ♠J and the ◇A, going one down.

'Ten points,' muttered Brother Tobias. 'It's not enough for 4NT.'

'Jack, jack, jack!' screeched the Parrot, drawing attention from the neighboring tables.

'What on earth is the bird on about?' queried Brother Tobias.

The Witchdoctor gave one of his trademark sniffs. 'He mos' probably meanin' you should play jack of spades to de ace on first round,' he said. 'With jack out of de way, you can finesse dummy's ten when diamonds break 4-0.'

'I say, that's very clever,' said Brother Luke. 'Did you follow that, Tobias? You unblock the jack on the first round, just as a precaution. Then you can prevent the Parrot's clever defense of going in with the queen.'

Brother Tobias glared at his partner. 'I believe it is parrots that are meant to repeat everything they hear,' he reprimanded, 'not missionaries who are foolishly playing bridge on a blazing hot day. Bring up the next board, will you?'

This was the second board of the round:

```
                    ♠ A K Q 10 6 4 3
                    ♡ K
                    ♢ 7 5
                    ♣ 6 5 2
♠ J 9 7 2                              ♠ 8 5
♡ 8 7 3          ┌──────────┐         ♡ Q 10 9 6 5 4 2
♢ J 10 6 3       │ EW Vul.  │         ♢ 9 2
♣ Q 4            │ Dealer N │         ♣ K 8
                 └──────────┘
                    ♠ —
                    ♡ A J
                    ♢ A K Q 8 4
                    ♣ A J 10 9 7 3
```

West	North	East	South
The	Brother	Witch-	Brother
Parrot	Luke	doctor	Tobias
	1♠	pass	2♣
pass	4♠	pass	6NT
all pass			

The Parrot led the ♡8, won in the dummy. Brother Tobias continued with the
♠A and ♠K, throwing two diamonds from his hand, but the jack refused to show.
He paused to consider his next move. If spades were 3-3, he could score an easy
overtrick by playing the ♠Q next. The alternative was to leave the ♠Q in dummy,
give up on the overtrick and play on clubs. If he could score five club tricks, along
with three diamonds and two tricks in each major, that would give him a total of
twelve.

Brother Tobias was unwilling to surrender the chance of an overtrick and a top
on the board. Even if the spade suit failed to break 3-3, there would still be a good
chance of setting up the clubs without allowing the dangerous defender — the one
with the ♠J — to gain the lead. 'Queen of spades, please,' he said.

A black honor card appeared from the Witchdoctor in the East seat. The sun
was glinting through the cola trees and for a moment Brother Tobias could not see
the card. He leaned forward and saw that it was the ♣K!

The Parrot followed with a low spade and Brother Tobias now had to turn to
the club suit for salvation. Had the Witchdoctor retained the ♣K, this could have
been done without allowing West on lead. Declarer would have led towards his
club holding. If the ♣K was played on the first round, he would allow the card to
win. Otherwise, he would have won with the ace and conceded the second round
of the suit to the Witchdoctor. As it was, the second round of clubs went to the
Parrot's queen. He was then able to cash the ♠J to beat the slam.

'That wasn't very clever, partner,' Brother Luke observed. 'You can make an easy twelve tricks without my queen of spades. Just leave it in dummy and play a club!'

'Heaven preserve us,' declared Brother Tobias. 'Obviously I would play it that way at IMPs. At pairs, everyone in 6♠ or 6NT would make an easy thirteen tricks when spades broke 3-3. Twelve tricks would give us a bottom.'

Brother Luke inspected the score sheet. 'Well, eleven tricks have certainly given us a bottom,' he announced. 'Everyone else played in clubs or spades.'

Brother Tobias produced a large white handkerchief and wiped the perspiration from his brow. He then leaned in the Parrot's direction. 'Cool me off with a few flaps of the wing, will you?' he said. 'It's not too much to ask after we've given you two tops.'

The Parrot and the Witchdoctor shared a glance. Given them two tops, did he say? It was typical of Brother Tobias to make no reference to the excellent defenses they had found. The insertion of the ♠Q on the first deal and the ♣K discard on the second? When had Brother Tobias ever defended in such sparkling fashion? Reluctantly, the Parrot gave a few feeble flaps of his right wing. He could hardly afford to get on the wrong side of Brother Tobias, not when he had the only key to the birdseed cupboard.

Quiz 29 *How would you play 6NT?*

```
            ♠ 6
            ♡ A K Q J 8 5
            ◊ 8 6 2
            ♣ J 6 5
♡ 10 led    ┌─────────────┐
            └─────────────┘
            ♠ A K Q J 8
            ♡ 7 2
            ◊ A Q 3
            ♣ K 8 3
```

West	North	East	South
	1♡	pass	1♠
2♣	2♡	pass	4NT
pass	5♠	pass	6NT
all pass			

To protect the ♣K from the opening lead, you choose 6NT as the final contract. How will you plan the play when West leads the ♡10, East following suit? (**The answer is on page 169**)

56. BERTIE BELLIS'S CLEVER PLAY

The Matron gave a small sigh as she took her seat against Bertie Bellis, the senior maths master. Had she ever scored a good board against him? Yes, there was one, that famous occasion when she had managed to defeat him in seven hearts. The look on his face when she had turned up with J10xx in the trump suit was one to treasure. Apart from that, though, he had led a charmed life against her.

Bertie Bellis smiled at the Matron. 'Has Stefan played well tonight?' he enquired.

The Matron glanced across at the young German master, a strong player who was on a one-year assignment at the school. 'Stefan hasn't played the game as long as we have,' she replied. 'Still, I expect he'll soon catch up with us.'

The players drew their cards for this deal:

```
                    ♠ K 7
                    ♡ A 7 6 2
                    ◇ 9 5 3
                    ♣ A K Q 6
  ♠ J 10 9 8 4 3 2                      ♠ Q 6 5
  ♡ —                  NS Vul.          ♡ K J 10 8 5 3
  ◇ J 10 8 6          Dealer E          ◇ —
  ♣ 10 7                                ♣ J 9 5 3
                    ♠ A
                    ♡ Q 9 4
                    ◇ A K Q 7 4 2
                    ♣ 8 4 2
```

West	North	East	South
The	*Percy*	*Stefan*	*Bertie*
Matron	*Cutforth*	*Götel*	*Bellis*
		2♡	3NT
pass	6NT	all pass	

The Matron was greatly relieved at the path the auction had taken. Thank goodness Bertie and Percy hadn't doubled two hearts! With only two jacks in the dummy, and no trumps at all, there was no way that Stefan would have made it.

The Matron led the ♠J against 6NT and down went the dummy. Bertie Bellis paused to assess his prospects. Unless diamonds broke 4-0, there were twelve tricks on top. An overtrick would then be his if clubs broke 3-3 or if East held four clubs and could be squeezed in hearts and clubs.

Many declarers would have ended their analysis at this point and cashed a top diamond to test the suit. Bertie Bellis took an extra moment to calculate what might happen if diamonds did break 4-0. In that case, a squeeze might be necessary just to make the contract. Playing ace and another diamond would not be good enough because the defender could win and return a third diamond. That would remove the last entry to his hand prematurely, before dummy's ♠K and ♡A had been cashed.

Bertie Bellis crossed to dummy with a club and led a diamond towards his hand, his eyes lighting up when East showed out. Thank goodness he had taken the trouble to plan the play! He ducked the trick to the Matron, knowing that a diamond return would now cause no problem; he would still have a diamond entry left to his hand. In fact, the Matron played another spade, won in the dummy. 'Ace of hearts, please,' said Bertie Bellis. He proceeded to run the remaining diamonds, arriving at this end position:

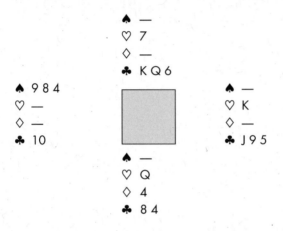

On the last diamond, declarer threw the ♡7 from dummy. 'Your play is too good, Bertie!' exclaimed Stefan Götel. He discarded the ♣5 and Bertie Bellis then scored three more club tricks for the contract.

'Nice play, ducking the first diamond,' observed Percy Cutforth. 'If you play ace and another, the Matron can beat you by returning a diamond.'

The Matron, who was not renowned for her skill in the post mortem, surveyed the scene blankly. 'I would have done,' she replied.

'If I throw the heart king instead, Matron, he makes the queen,' Stefan Götel explained.

The Matron consoled her partner with a smile. 'I'd probably have got it wrong, too,' she replied. 'Bertie's always lucky against me. You mustn't blame yourself!'

```
                        ♠ 6
                        ♡ A K Q J 8 5
                        ◊ 8 6 2
                        ♣ J 6 5
      ♠ 9 4                              ♠ 10 7 5 3 2
      ♡ 10                               ♡ 9 6 4 3
      ◊ K J 7 4                          ◊ 10 9 5
      ♣ A Q 10 9 4 2                     ♣ 7
                        ♠ A K Q J 8
                        ♡ 7 2
                        ◊ A Q 3
                        ♣ K 8 3
```

West	North	East	South
	1♡	pass	1♠
2♣	2♡	pass	4NT
pass	5♠	pass	6NT
all pass			

South bids Roman Keycard Blackwood, with hearts temporarily agreed as trumps. North's 5♠ response shows two keycards (probably the ace and king of trumps) along with the queen of trumps. To protect the ♣K from the opening lead, South then chooses 6NT as the final contract. How will you plan the play when West leads the ♡10, East following suit?

All will be well if the spades break 4-3. After winning the heart lead, you play three top spades, discovering that East holds a guard in the suit. What now? You have eleven top tricks and must decide who holds the ◊K. If it is East, a diamond finesse will give you a twelfth trick. However, West's vulnerable overcall suggests that he holds the ◊K. What can you do in that case?

You can arrange an endplay on West, provided you cash your winners in the right order. The first step is to play the last spade winner in your hand. You then return to dummy and play the remaining heart winners. Your last three cards are the ◊AQ and the ♣K. What can West keep? If he retains the bare ♣A and the guarded ◊K, you will throw him in with a club. If instead he bares the ◊K, you can play the ◊A to drop that card. In practice, you are unlikely to have any problem in guessing which cards West has retained.

57. PROFESSOR BARCLAY'S INVITATION

The Monastery of St. Titus entertained few visitors. The Abbot regarded them as a nuisance, distracting the monks from their work, prayers and post-mortems. A notable exception was the rotund figure of Professor Barclay, who visited the monastery every summer to 'recharge his batteries'. Not only did the Abbot welcome the chance to share the company of a man whose intellectual brilliance matched his own, but the Professor always brought a case of top-quality claret with him. How often did you get the chance to taste twenty-year-old claret nowadays? The local supermarkets thought they were doing you a favor if they put a three-year-old bottle on their shelves.

Although the Professor was no great expert at the game, the Abbot always insisted on partnering him for the Thursday duplicate. The session would be followed by a lengthy discussion of the deals, back in the Abbot's study, accompanied by the uncorking of some distinguished bottle.

'You do play that a four-club bid is always Gerber, don't you?' enquired the Professor, who was filling out a convention card.

The Abbot gritted his teeth. The Gerber convention was one of his pet hates. 'Of course, Donald,' he replied. 'We don't want to bid any slams with two aces missing.'

Three or four rounds into the session, the black-bearded Brother Zac arrived at the table. A somewhat rustic bidder, he was nevertheless a sound player of the cards. This was the first board of the round:

```
                      ♠ Q 7
                      ♡ Q
                      ◇ Q 10 9 5 3 2
                      ♣ K 7 4 2
    ♠ 9                                   ♠ J 10 8 5 4 2
    ♡ K 10 9 8 4      EW Vul.             ♡ 7 6 2
    ◇ 8 7 4           Dealer W            ◇ J
    ♣ A 8 6 3                             ♣ J 10 5
                      ♠ A K 6 3
                      ♡ A J 5 3
                      ◇ A K 6
                      ♣ Q 9
```

West	North	East	South
Professor	Brother	The	Brother
Barclay	Fabius	Abbot	Zac
2♡	pass	pass	3NT
pass	4◇	pass	6NT
all pass			

Professor Barclay opened with a weak 2♡ and a few moments later Brother Zac had installed himself in 6NT. He won the diamond opening lead with the ace and led the ♣9 toward dummy's king. The Professor could not afford to go in with the ace or declarer would have twelve tricks. Dummy's ♣K won and Brother Zac now ran five more diamond tricks, throwing two hearts and a spade from his hand. He cashed the ♠Q and ♠A to leave this ending:

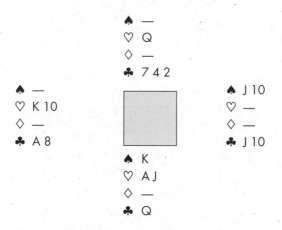

When Brother Zac led the ♠K, West discarded the ♣8 and the blocking ♡Q was thrown from dummy. A club to the Professor's bare ace forced him to lead into South's heart tenace and twelve tricks had been made.

'You opened a vulnerable weak-two on a five-card suit?' exclaimed the Abbot. 'A child in a kindergarten would make the slam after that. You might as well have shown him your cards.'

'A weak-two opening is perfectly normal on my hand,' replied the Professor. 'All our students bid that way, back at Warwick.'

'Opening on a five-card suit might in fact have caused me to go wrong in the endgame,' observed Brother Zac. 'If the Professor bares the king of hearts and keeps ace and another club, I might throw him in with a club, thinking he still has two hearts left.'

'I was planning to do that,' the Professor replied. 'Unfortunately the Abbot had thrown three hearts, exposing the position.'

The Abbot refrained from any further comment, not wishing to put his half-share of some worthy bottle at risk. 'Sorry, partner,' he said.

The next round brought the ill-groomed novice, Brother Cameron, to the Abbot's table. The Abbot delivered a warning glance in the youngster's direction, making it clear that the valued visitor should be given an easy ride. This was the first board that they played:

```
              ♠ Q 8 6 5 2
              ♡ K 5
              ◇ K Q J 4
              ♣ 10 3
♠ 4                              ♠ A K 9 7
♡ J 3          ┌─────────┐      ♡ Q 9 8 6 2
◇ 9 8 7 5 3    │Both Vul.│      ◇ 6 2
♣ 9 7 6 4 2    │Dealer S │      ♣ 8 5
               └─────────┘
              ♠ J 10 3
              ♡ A 10 7 4
              ◇ A 10
              ♣ A K Q J
```

West	North	East	South
Professor	Brother	The	Brother
Barclay	Damien	Abbot	Cameron
			2NT
pass	3♡	pass	4♠
pass	6♠	dbl	pass
pass	6NT	dbl	all pass

Looking favorably on his three tens, Brother Cameron opened a 20-22 point 2NT. When his partner made a transfer response, showing spades, Brother Cameron upgraded his hand once more, breaking the transfer. The Abbot surveyed his opponents disdainfully when a spade slam was reached. How many times had he taught these youngsters not to jump to a slam without using Blackwood? In these days of Roman Keycard Blackwood, there was absolutely no excuse for bidding a slam with the ace and king of trumps missing. Still, at least it would be a welcome top for the Professor's scorecard.

When the Abbot doubled the small slam in spades, Brother Damien amended the contract to 6NT. The Abbot doubled again and it was Professor Barclay to lead.

'Sorry, I wasn't paying attention there,' said the Professor. 'May I ask what was the first suit bid by the dummy?'

The Abbot looked anxiously at his partner. What on earth was he talking about?

'My partner opened 2NT and I responded Three Hearts,' replied Brother Damien.

'I did alert it,' added Brother Cameron.

'Ah, hearts, thank you,' said Professor Barclay.

The Professor led the ♡J and down went the dummy. Brother Cameron surveyed it for a few seconds, before moving into action. 'King, please,' he said.

The lank-haired novice cashed four rounds of clubs, throwing two spades from the dummy, and then turned to the diamonds. This end position arose:

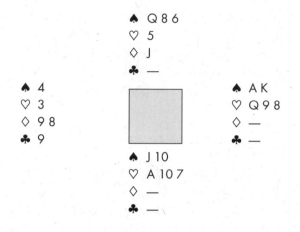

♠ Q 8 6
♡ 5
◇ J
♣ —

♠ 4   ♠ A K
♡ 3   ♡ Q 9 8
◇ 9 8   ◇ —
♣ 9   ♣ —

♠ J 10
♡ A 10 7
◇ —
♣ —

When dummy's last diamond was played, the Abbot had no good discard. If he released a top spade, declarer would throw the ♡7 and set up the spades. Hoping that his partner held the ♡10, the Abbot discarded a heart. Brother Cameron threw a spade from the South hand and finessed the ♡10. His last two hearts were now good and the slam had been made.

Vintage claret or no vintage claret, the Abbot was not going to let this appalling opening lead pass by. 'Jack doubleton is the worst lead in the game, Professor!' he cried. 'Lead any of the other three suits and he doesn't have a prayer of a chance.'

'Yes, my fault,' the Professor replied. 'At Warwick University some of us play a method known as the Lightner Double. You would probably find it too fancy, but the idea is that you double when you want the lead of dummy's first suit.'

The Abbot winced. 'Everyone plays that,' he said. 'It doesn't apply when dummy's first bid was a transfer, surely?'

'I don't see why not,' replied the Professor. 'You didn't mean your double of six spades to ask for a spade lead, did you?'

'Playing that the double asks for a heart lead makes good sense,' observed Brother Cameron. 'It's a similar idea to the Rosenkranz double of a splinter bid.'

'Bright lads, you have here, Abbot,' declared the Professor. He directed a kindly eye on the two opponents. 'Would you two boys like to join us for a drink afterwards?'

The Abbot's mouth fell open and he made frenzied shaking movements of the head, indicating to the two novices that they should decline the invitation.

'That's very kind of you,' replied Brother Cameron. 'We'll look forward to it.'

'See you in the Abbot's study after the game, then,' continued the Professor. 'I brought my last bottle of 1975 Chateau Montrose with me. I'll be most interested to hear what you boys think of it!'

58. THE RABBI'S UNEXPECTED LOSER

'It worked again!' said David, arriving at the Rabbi's house for a men's four.

'What's that?' enquired the Rabbi.

'I take a taxi here tonight,' David replied. 'I get out of the taxi, fumble in my pockets for some money and then open the back door of the taxi again and begin searching the floor. I must have dropped a 50-pound note, I tell the driver. I will borrow a torch from my friend to look for it.'

'So?' asked the Rabbi.

'Just two steps from the taxi, I take,' continued David, 'and off it goes at full speed! Another free trip.'

The Rabbi shook his head disapprovingly. 'A sad indictment of our taxi drivers,' he declared. 'Come inside. It is cold here.'

The game began and it was not long before the Rabbi arrived in a slam.

```
                    ♠ Q 8 2
                    ♡ —
                    ◇ A K J 6
                    ♣ A Q J 10 7 3
  ♠ A J 10 9 5 3                      ♠ 4
  ♡ J 6            Both Vul.          ♡ 10 9 8 7 5 4 2
  ◇ 10 9           Dealer W           ◇ 8 7 4
  ♣ K 8 2                             ♣ 9 5
                    ♠ K 7 6
                    ♡ A K Q 3
                    ◇ Q 5 3 2
                    ♣ 6 4
```

West	North	East	South
Eric	Sam	David	The Rabbi
2♠	dbl	pass	3NT
pass	6NT	all pass	

Eric led the ◇10 and down went the dummy. 'You bid 6NT with a heart void?' he queried. 'That is good bidding, you think?'

'If it wasn't a good bid, I wouldn't make it,' Sam replied. He tapped the side of his nose. 'In 6♣ or 6◇ there would be a spade ruff. I can smell it.'

The Rabbi won the ◇10 lead with dummy's ace, East playing the ◇4. He was fairly sure that Eric would hold the ♣K as part of his vulnerable weak two-bid. With just one entry to the South hand, the ◇Q, only a single club finesse would be possible. Good enough if Eric held ♣Kx, but what if he held ♣Kxx?

At Trick 2 the Rabbi led dummy's ♠Q. If West were to capture this, the ♠K would be a second entry to the South hand and two club finesses could be taken.

Eric allowed dummy's ♠Q to win. 'I know I learnt bridge only yesterday, Rabbi,' he said. 'But it was early in the morning. I have played long enough, in the meantime, to see through some of your tricks.'

The Rabbi continued with dummy's ◇K and led the ◇6 on the third round. When East's ◇8 appeared, he followed with the ◇5 from his hand! David now had to lead either a heart or a club. When he chose a heart, the Rabbi won with the ♡A and discarded a spade from dummy. He then took advantage of the entry to finesse the ♣Q successfully. Returning to his hand with the ◇Q, he cashed another top heart, discarding dummy's last spade loser and finessed the ♣J. Everyone followed and the Rabbi was able to claim the contract.

'I made a trick, can you believe it?' exclaimed David. 'The highest card in my hand was a ten and I made a trick against a slam!'

'That's why the Rabbi made the slam,' Eric observed. 'Without your assistance he couldn't have taken two club finesses.'

The Rabbi nodded. 'The four of diamonds was the most precious card in your hand, David,' he said. 'Play the seven and eight on the first two rounds and you defeat me. When I lead dummy's six, you will underplay with the four.'

David had barely followed the explanation but that did not stop him from admiring the Rabbi's play. 'To avoid paying a taxi driver is easy,' he said. 'To avoid paying the Rabbi after a game of bridge? That is more difficult!'

Quiz 30 *How would you play 6NT?*

```
              ♠ A Q 7 6 4
              ♡ K Q J 7
              ◇ A 6
              ♣ J 6
◇Q led        ┌──────────┐
              └──────────┘
              ♠ J 5
              ♡ A 6 5
              ◇ K 5 3
              ♣ A K 7 5 4
```

West	North	East	South
			1NT
pass	2♣	pass	2◇
pass	3♡	pass	3NT
pass	6NT	all pass	

How will you play 6NT when West leads the ◇Q? **(The answer is overleaf.)**

```
                    ♠ A Q 7 6 4
                    ♡ K Q J 7
                    ◇ A 6
                    ♣ J 6
    ♠ 9 2                           ♠ K 10 8 3
    ♡ 10 9 3                        ♡ 8 4 2
    ◇ Q J 10 8                      ◇ 9 7 4 2
    ♣ Q 10 9 3                      ♣ 8 2
                    ♠ J 5
                    ♡ A 6 5
                    ◇ K 5 3
                    ♣ A K 7 5 4
```

West	North	East	South
			1NT
pass	2♣	pass	2◇
pass	3♡	pass	3NT
pass	6NT	all pass	

North shows five spades and four hearts, using the Smolen convention (where responder bids his shorter major on the second round, to allow partner to play the contract when there is a fit in the longer major). How will you play 6NT when West leads the ◇Q?

You have nine tricks on top and a chance of developing extra tricks in both the black suits. Which black suit should you attack first? You should play on spades first, because only that suit gives you a chance of establishing the three extra tricks that you need.

You win the diamond lead with dummy's ace and lead a low spade towards the jack. If East plays his ♠K on thin air, you will have four spade tricks, enough for the contract. Let's say that East plays low. The ♠J wins the trick and you now have ten top tricks. The best continuation is a low club towards the jack (yes, there is a pleasing similarity between the plays in the two black suits!). If West rises with the ♣Q, he will give you four club tricks, enough for the slam. Perhaps he will play low, allowing dummy's jack to win. Your trick total has now grown to eleven. You play a club to the ace, everyone following, and can now play king and another club to set up your twelfth trick.

(If the ♠J had lost to the ♠Q with West, you would have needed the spade suit to break 3-3.)

59. BROTHER TOBIAS'S THOUGHTFUL DEFENSE

The final of the Bozwambi pairs championship was a 28-board session, with just six tables in play. Some members of the community played a very wild game indeed, which did tend to lower the tone of the normal duplicates. Few such contestants had qualified for the final and Brother Tobias was looking forward to a rare afternoon of top-class bridge. His first opponents were the favorites to win the event, the Witchdoctor and Mbozi.

```
                    ♠ 7 5 2
                    ♡ Q 9 7 4 2
                    ♢ J 7 5 2
                    ♣ A
   ♠ 8 4                              ♠ J 10 9 3
   ♡ 10 3          ┌─────────┐        ♡ J 8 6 5
   ♢ Q 9 6 4       │ NS Vul. │        ♢ 3
   ♣ J 10 9 3 2    │ Dealer S│        ♣ Q 8 6 4
                   └─────────┘
                    ♠ A K Q 6
                    ♡ A K
                    ♢ A K 10 8
                    ♣ K 7 5
```

West	North	East	South
Brother	Mbozi	Brother	Witch-
Tobias		Luke	doctor
			2♣
pass	2♢	pass	3NT
pass	6NT	all pass	

Brother Tobias led the ♣J and surveyed the dummy with no great approval. 'Very lazily bid, Mbozi,' he declared. 'You might have had a good fit in either red suit.'

Mbozi looked sullenly at the overweight missionary. 'No way to biddin' de hearts,' he replied. 'He mos' probably passin' 4♡ bid.'

'To do well at bridge, you have to put a bit of effort into building your system,' Brother Tobias persisted. 'We play that 4♣ asks for suits in ascending order. The responses of 4♢ and 4♡ are major-suit transfers. Here you would start with 4♢.'

'Do we play transfers over a 3NT rebid?' Brother Luke queried. 'It's news to me.'

Brother Tobias winced at this indiscretion from his second-in-command. How on earth could he ever teach the locals to play well with so little backing from his colleague? 'Brother Luke will have his little joke,' he continued. 'A thorough knowledge of one's bidding system is an absolute essential to playing the game well.'

The Witchdoctor won the club lead with dummy's ace and played a diamond to the ten and West's queen. He won the club continuation and unblocked the ♡A and ♡K. When he played ◊A and ◊K, East discarded two clubs. These cards remained:

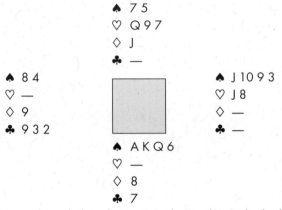

```
                    ♠ 7 5
                    ♡ Q 9 7
                    ◊ J
                    ♣ —
     ♠ 8 4                            ♠ J 10 9 3
     ♡ —                              ♡ J 8
     ◊ 9                              ◊ —
     ♣ 9 3 2                          ♣ —
                    ♠ A K Q 6
                    ♡ —
                    ◊ 8
                    ♣ 7
```

When a diamond was led to dummy's jack, Brother Luke had no good discard in the East seat. Since a heart discard would obviously cost the contract, he threw the ♠3. The Witchdoctor cashed the ♡Q, discarding his club loser. The hearts failed to break 3-3 but better luck came from the spades. The ace, king and queen drew the defenders' remaining cards and the ♠6 gave him the slam.

'Very fortunate,' Brother Tobias declared. 'More luck than you deserved, really, after such an auction.'

The Witchdoctor turned his yellow eyes in Brother Tobias's direction. 'Hold up de diamond queen and you beatin' it,' he said.

Brother Luke nodded. 'Yes, I was wondering that,' he said. 'By taking the queen, you set up dummy's jack as an entry.'

'We can do without these double-dummy observations,' Brother Tobias exclaimed. 'Give declarer another heart and he would have twelve top tricks. Ducking the diamond would give him an overtrick and a complete top.'

Mbozi offered the scoresheet for Brother Tobias's inspection. 'Takin' de diamond give us a complete top too!' he announced. 'You wanna see it?'

'Gloating over a lucky result is nasty habit of yours, Mbozi,' reprimanded Brother Tobias. 'You would do well to follow the example of impeccable ethics set by Brother Luke and myself.'

Mbozi sat back resentfully in his chair. 'Last week you callin' Brother Luke blidderin' clodpole, whatever dat is,' he replied. 'You want me to followin' dat example?'

'That was an exceptional situation,' declared Brother Tobias. 'It could hardly have been more obvious to lead a trump from his hand!'

60. BROTHER AELRED'S ANALYSIS

During September the monks of St. Titus scoured the surrounding countryside for blackberries. Each monk was set an individual quota, according to his age and monasterial duties. A novice, for example, might have to pick fifty pounds of blackberries. Someone like the 82-year-old Brother Jacob or the hard-working monastery chef, Brother Anthony, would be set a nominal target of perhaps two or three pounds.

'I made a really brilliant play last week,' said Brother Sextus, detaching a long bramble that had become entangled in his cassock.

Brother Aelred was picking rapidly with both hands, dropping the berries into a cardboard box at his feet. 'By mistake, presumably?' he said.

'Very humorous,' replied Brother Sextus. 'If you're so clever, let's see how well you do.' He handed Brother Aelred a scorecard with this diagram inscribed on the back:

```
        ♠ A 6
        ♡ J 10 7
        ◇ K Q 10 7
        ♣ A K 5 3
        ━━━━━━━━━
        ♠ K Q 7
        ♡ A 6 3
        ◇ A J 8
        ♣ Q 7 6 4
```

'How do you play 6NT on a spade lead?' asked Brother Sextus, leaning forward at a dangerous angle to reach a particularly juicy clump of fruit.

'Mind those stinging nettles,' warned Brother Aelred.

'Aargh!' cried Brother Sextus, retreating from the bush with his right hand painfully aloft.

Brother Aelred studied the diagram. 'I win with the ace of spades and cash the ace-king of clubs,' he said. 'They don't break?'

'No, West has four clubs,' replied Brother Sextus.

'Well, I'll make the slam when the heart honors are split,' declared Brother Aelred. 'I cross to a diamond and lead a low heart toward dummy's jack-ten. If West goes in, I can finesse against East's honor on the next round. If West chooses to play low, I can squeeze him in hearts and clubs.'

Brother Sextus blinked in surprise. Brother Aelred had never been known to squeeze anyone except himself.

'Of course if East had turned up with four clubs I would have to lead the jack of hearts from dummy instead. If East covers, I win and set up a second heart trick by leading toward the ten. If he doesn't, he's the one who gets squeezed in hearts and clubs.'

Brother Sextus could hardly believe what he was hearing. 'I'd have laid a chapel to a candle against you getting that one right,' he said.

Brother Aelred moved his cardboard box to a new patch of brambles, nodding approvingly at the heavily laden branches. 'That's a bit harsh,' he replied. 'I nearly got it right when you showed it to me yesterday!'

Quiz 31 *How would you play 6NT?*

```
                    ♠ Q 9 6 4
                    ♡ J 7 3
                    ◇ 7 5 2
                    ♣ 7 4 3
  ♣10 led         ┌──────────────┐
                  └──────────────┘
                    ♠ A K
                    ♡ A Q 5
                    ◇ A K Q 3
                    ♣ A K Q J
```

West	North	East	South
			2♣
pass	2◇	pass	6NT
all pass			

Sitting South, you pick up the biggest hand of your life. Is it a dream? No, the honor cards remain there in front of your eyes, fully in focus. How will you play 6NT when West leads the ♣10 to your ace? **(The answer is on page 183.)**

61. SISTER KATE'S WEAK TWO-BID

The mere sight of the Mother of Discipline's black punishment book was enough to strike fear in the novices' hearts. The slightest departure from correct etiquette, when playing against her, would result in one day on St. Iona's Regime. The offender would have to remain silent for 24 hours, sleep without a pillow and eat her morning cereal with no milk on it. 'There's no need to look so aghast,' the Mother of Discipline would say, on awarding such a punishment. 'Don't forget that St. Iona spent her whole life on the Regime. An inspiring example to us all!'

With some trepidation the two new novices, Sister Kate and Sister Juliet, took their seats at the Mother of Discipline's table. 'Good evening, Reverend Mother,' they chimed in unison. 'We hope you're having an enjoyable session tonight.'

With a brief nod, the Mother of Discipline acknowledged this rendering of the approved pre-round greeting. She extracted her cards for the first board.

```
                      ♠ J 8
                      ♡ J 10 5 4 2
                      ◇ K 8 7 2
                      ♣ A 3
  ♠ A Q 10 5 3 2              ♠ 7 6 4
  ♡ Q 7 3        Neither Vul.  ♡ 9 6
  ◇ 4            Dealer W      ◇ 10 9 6 5 3
  ♣ 8 7 5                      ♣ 9 6 2
                      ♠ K 9
                      ♡ A K 8
                      ◇ A Q J
                      ♣ K Q J 10 4
```

West	North	East	South
Sister	Sister	Sister	Mother of
Kate	Thomas	Juliet	Discipline
2♠	pass	pass	dbl
pass	4♡	pass	4NT
pass	5◇	pass	6NT
all pass			

Before opening the bidding, Sister Kate checked carefully that her hand conformed to the weak-two guidelines in the Novices' Handbook. The hand had to be in the 6-10 point range, the trump suit must include two of the three top honors and you were not allowed to have a four-card side suit. Yes, it seemed that even the Mother of Discipline would be pressed to find fault with this particular hand. At any other table, of course, the novices would open a weak-two whenever they felt like it.

Sister Kate opened 2♠ and a few moments later found herself on lead against

6NT. She led a safe ♣8 and down went the dummy. The Mother of Discipline peered at dummy's cards through her thick lenses, counting eleven top tricks. East was the initial favorite to hold the ♡Q and a successful heart finesse would bring her total to twelve. Since the diamond suit was blocked, she won the club opening lead with the king in her hand, retaining dummy's ace as an entry. She then cashed the ♢A and ♢Q, West showing out on the second round. Ah, that changed things! Assuming young Sister Kate was following the convent's strict rules on weak-two openings, her distribution must be 6-3-1-3. Indeed, even if she had been allowed to hold a four-card side suit, the odds would still be high that she held 3-3 shape in the unknown suits. With West now known to hold three hearts to her partner's two, she had become the favorite to hold the ♡Q.

The Mother of Discipline played her third diamond winner and crossed to the ♣A. She then cashed the ♢K, throwing the ♠9 from her hand. A heart to the ace was followed by her remaining club winners, leading to this end position:

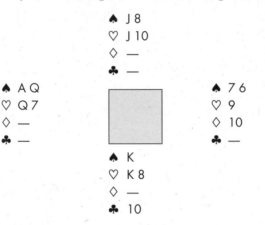

```
                    ♠ J 8
                    ♡ J 10
                    ♢ —
                    ♣ —
   ♠ A Q                            ♠ 7 6
   ♡ Q 7                            ♡ 9
   ♢ —                             ♢ 10
   ♣ —                             ♣ —
                    ♠ K
                    ♡ K 8
                    ♢ —
                    ♣ 10
```

When the ♣10 was led, Sister Kate had no easy discard in the West seat. She eventually decided to throw the ♠Q. The Mother of Discipline discarded a spade from dummy and exited with the ♠K to West's ace. She claimed the last two tricks on the enforced heart return and the small slam was hers.

'Well played indeed, Reverend Mother,' exclaimed Sister Kate. 'How did you know that I held the ♡Q? I would still have had six points without it.'

'Goodness, child, it made no difference where the ♡Q was,' the Mother of Discipline replied. 'If you keep two cards in hearts, the throw-in will work whoever holds the queen. If you throw a heart instead, the suit will be 2-2 and the queen will drop.'

Sister Kate had been unable to follow all this but to say so openly might imply that the Mother of Discipline's explanation had been unclear. The black book was then certain to make an appearance. 'Yes, I see, Reverend Mother,' she said.

Sister Kate and Sister Juliet shared a brief glance. One board down, one to go. If they could negotiate the second board safely, all would be well. They would sleep with a pillow tonight!

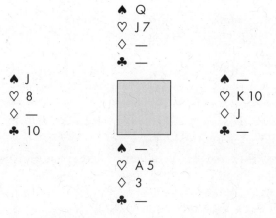

	♠ Q964	
	♡ J73	
	◇ 752	
	♣ 743	
♠ J1075		♠ 832
♡ 82		♡ K10964
◇ 86		◇ J1094
♣ 109862		♣ 5
	♠ AK	
	♡ AQ5	
	◇ AKQ3	
	♣ AKQJ	

West	North	East	South
			2♣
pass	2◇	pass	6NT
all pass			

How will you play 6NT when West leads the ♣10, won with the ♣A?

There is no hurry to test the diamonds. You cash a second round of clubs, East discarding a heart, and continue with the ♡Q. If a defender wins with the ♡K, dummy's ♡J will provide an entry to the blocked spade winner.

Let's suppose that East manages to read the situation, allowing your ♡Q to win. You cash your remaining black-suit winners and then test the diamonds. West shows out on the third round but the contract is still secure! These cards remain:

	♠ Q	
	♡ J7	
	◇ —	
	♣ —	
♠ J		♠ —
♡ 8		♡ K10
◇ —		◇ J
♣ 10		♣ —
	♠ —	
	♡ A5	
	◇ 3	
	♣ —	

You lead the ◇3, discarding dummy's ♠Q. East has to win and lead from the ♡K. Just as well! It would be a shame to go minus with a giant hand like that.

62. LOOSE LILLIAN'S CLEVER PLAY

The Sheriff and Sir Guy of Gisburne were entertaining a couple of tarts from Lucas Street. Aiming to make a long evening of it, they decided to begin with an hour or so at the bridge table. 'I will partner Loose Lillian for the bridge,' declared the Sheriff. 'You can partner the charming young Meg, Gisburne. When it comes to the main business of the evening, later, we can swap partners.'

'But, my Lord!' protested Gisburne. 'Surely Madam Brockett aimed to match the women to our ages. For the main business, Meg must be intended for me.'

'You seem to be forgetting who paid the two shillings,' reprimanded the Sheriff. 'Madam Brockett knows my tastes.'

Loose Lillian, who had lost most of her teeth at an early age, leered at Gisburne. 'You will have no cause to complain, Sir,' she said.

The game began and Loose Lillian was soon in a slam.

```
                    ♠ Q 9 7 3
                    ♡ A 7
                    ◇ K Q 8 7 4
                    ♣ 4 3
    ♠ J 10 8 4                      ♠ 6 2
    ♡ Q 9 3        Neither Vul.     ♡ 10 8 5 4
    ◇ J 9 5 3      Dealer N         ◇ 10 6 2
    ♣ K 9                           ♣ J 10 8 7
                    ♠ A K 5
                    ♡ K J 6 2
                    ◇ A
                    ♣ A Q 6 5 2
```

West	North	East	South
Guy of	The	Meg	Loose
Gisburne	Sheriff		Lillian
	1◇	pass	2♣
pass	2◇	pass	6NT
all pass			

Gisburne led the ♠J and down went the dummy.

'Well bid, my Lord,' exclaimed Loose Lillian. 'I like a man who opens on 11 points. Particularly when he puts down such a useful nine of spades!'

The Sheriff laughed. 'Gisburne always gives a trick away on the lead.'

Loose Lillian won the ♠A and paused to assess her prospects. She had ten tricks on top, counting four spade tricks with a finesse of the nine. An eleventh could come from the diamond suit, if it broke 4-3. She would then need a successful finesse in either hearts or clubs. Wait though — if Gisburne held four diamonds, she would be able to endplay him for a twelfth trick! Gisburne was none too pleased. He and the Sheriff were playing for a groat-a-100 stake. Hardly a substantial amount, but with the inexperienced Meg opposite, though, his losses could mount up.

Loose Lillian unblocked the ◇A and played the ♠K, everyone following. A finesse of the ♠9 proved successful, as expected, and she continued with the ♠Q. Both defenders followed to the ◇K and ◇Q. When she played a fourth round of diamonds, throwing a club from her hand, Gisburne won the trick. He then had to return a heart or a club into one of South's tenaces. He chose to play a heart, won with the jack, and Loose Lillian was then able to reach dummy's thirteenth diamond with the ♡A.

The Sheriff laughed heartily. 'Very amusing!' he exclaimed. 'The great Sir Guy of Gisburne, endplayed by a shilling tart from Lucas Street.'

'You are unfair, my Lord,' Gisburne protested. 'The spade jack was an obvious lead and there was nothing I could do from that point.'

'Endplayed by a shilling tart,' repeated the Sheriff, his tongue lingering on the words. 'How the court will enjoy the story tomorrow!'

It was the third rubber when Gisburne had a chance to regain his reputation.

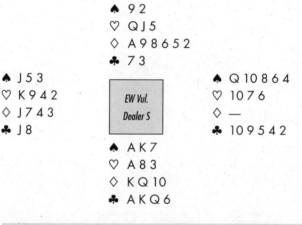

	♠ 9 2	
	♡ Q J 5	
	◇ A 9 8 6 5 2	
	♣ 7 3	

♠ J 5 3	EW Vul.	♠ Q 10 8 6 4
♡ K 9 4 2	Dealer S	♡ 10 7 6
◇ J 7 4 3		◇ —
♣ J 8		♣ 10 9 5 4 2

	♠ A K 7	
	♡ A 8 3	
	◇ K Q 10	
	♣ A K Q 6	

West	North	East	South
The Sheriff	Meg	Loose Lillian	Guy of Gisburne
			2♣
pass	2◇	pass	3NT
pass	6NT	all pass	

The Sheriff had rarely seen a less attractive collection of suits from which to lead. The well-known guideline, 'Only a knave would lead from a jack' came to mind. If a lead from one of his jacks proved costly, the surrendered trick was unlikely to return. Strangely, it could prove safer to lead a heart from the king. Even if this allowed declarer to score two early tricks in the suit, he might still live to enjoy the king. The Sheriff tossed the ♡2 on to the table and down went the dummy.

'Some would bid six diamonds on my hand,' Meg observed. 'But I bid it in notrump so that you could play it, Sir Guy.'

Gisburne nodded approvingly. The wench showed good judgment, for someone so young. It was a pity she would not be delivering her other skills in his direction, once the card game was over. He played the ♡Q from dummy and this card won the trick. When he continued with a low diamond towards his hand, he could not believe his bad luck when East showed out, throwing a club. Keeping his wits about him, Gisburne played the ◇10 from his hand. If the Sheriff could be tempted to win with the ◇J, he would be able to overtake with dummy's ◇A on the third round and score the five diamond tricks that were needed for the slam.

The Sheriff chuckled openly. 'I am the one player in the shire capable of reading your mind, Gisburne,' he declared. 'The three of diamonds from me.'

Gisburne slumped in his chair. A plague on this session! It was not as if some great consolation awaited him at the end of it. The only remaining chance was to endplay the Sheriff with a diamond to lead away from the ♡K. Gisburne played his winners in the black suits, cashed the ◇K and overtook the ◇Q with the ◇A:

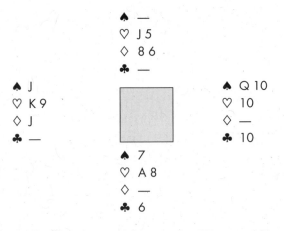

Gisburne exited with a diamond, hoping that West would have nothing but hearts and be forced to give dummy an entry with the ♡J. Any such hope was dispelled when East discarded the ♡10 on the trick. The Sheriff won with the ◇J and led the ♠J. East overtook with the ♠Q and the slam was three down.

'Bid six diamonds, you young strumpet!' Gisburne exploded. 'I'faith, I've rarely seen such poor bidding. Do they teach you nothing in Lucas Street?'

Meg blinked back a few tears. 'Sorry, Sir,' she replied. 'Loose Lillian, here, teaches us new girls. She said we should let the gentleman play the hands.'

'You can throw six diamonds at the wall,' Gisburne continued. 'King and queen of trumps, run the ten and you can enter the long diamond hand with a spade ruff to draw the last trump.'

Loose Lillian, who felt some responsibility for the young girl in her charge, leaned forward. 'All the Lucas Street girls would bid 6NT on her hand,' she said. 'Should you not have made the contract?'

The Sheriff sucked in his cheeks. Wonderful! Not only did he have a very pleasurable couple of hours with young Meg in prospect, it seemed that Gisburne's agony was not yet at an end.

'Suppose you win the heart lead with the ace, Sir Guy,' Loose Lillian continued. 'You continue with the king, queen and ten of diamonds, running the card, and can then set up an entry to dummy by playing a heart.'

'An obvious line of play,' declared the Sheriff. 'How could you miss it?'

Loose Lillian smiled at the Sheriff. 'Brilliant opening lead, my Lord,' she declared. 'If declarer doesn't waste his entry at Trick 1, he can't go wrong.'

'I have few equals when it comes to opening leads,' declared the Sheriff. Suddenly he rose to his feet. 'Enough of this secondary pastime!' he exclaimed. 'Come, Meg. You must show me what the King's shilling buys nowadays.'

'But, my Lord, I am behind in the game,' protested Gisburne. 'The rubber is not finished. Etiquette demands that you must give me a chance to recover.'

The Sheriff was not listening. With the willing young Meg at his side, he disappeared into his stateroom. Like a wildcat approaching its prey, Loose Lillian moved towards Gisburne. 'What a big, strong man you are,' she declared. 'Let me get to work and in two minutes you'll have forgotten all about your bridge losses.'

Perhaps the evening would not be so bad, thought Gisburne. 'A woman of your experience has no doubt picked up a few tricks over the years,' he said.

'You're not wrong there,' Loose Lillian replied. 'Twenty-four years I've worked in Lucas Street, not that you'd guess it. In all that time only two men have asked for their shilling back!'

Quiz 32 *How would you play 6NT?*

```
                    ♠ K Q 6
                    ♡ A Q 5
                    ◊ A J 9 5
                    ♣ Q 7 3
    ♣J led          ┌─────────┐
                    └─────────┘
                    ♠ A 9 7
                    ♡ K 7 6 4
                    ◊ K Q 7 2
                    ♣ A 6
```

West	North	East	South
			1NT
pass	6NT	all pass	

How will you play the slam when West leads the ♣J? **(Answer is overleaf.)**

```
                        ♠ K Q 6
                        ♡ A Q 5
                        ◇ A J 9 5
                        ♣ Q 7 3
        ♠ 10 5 4 2                     ♠ J 8 3
        ♡ 10 2                         ♡ J 9 8 3
        ◇ 4 3                          ◇ 10 8 6
        ♣ J 10 9 5 4                   ♣ K 8 2
                        ♠ A 9 7
                        ♡ K 7 6 4
                        ◇ K Q 7 2
                        ♣ A 6
```

West	North	East	South
			1NT
pass	6NT	all pass	

West leads the ♣J. You have eleven tricks on top and must seek one more from hearts or clubs. All will be well if the hearts break 3-3. There is also the chance of a squeeze if the same defender holds four or more hearts and the sole club guard.

Unless West is the village idiot (some bridge writers are more tactful than others), you can be confident that East holds the ♣K and should therefore play low from dummy on the first trick. Just in case the squeeze is on, you should also play low from your hand. You win the second round of clubs, East following with a spot card, and cash your winners in the pointed suits. This end position results:

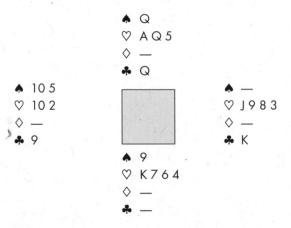

```
                        ♠ Q
                        ♡ A Q 5
                        ◇ —
                        ♣ Q
        ♠ 10 5                        ♠ —
        ♡ 10 2                        ♡ J 9 8 3
        ◇ —                           ◇ —
        ♣ 9                           ♣ K
                        ♠ 9
                        ♡ K 7 6 4
                        ◇ —
                        ♣ —
```

When you play dummy's ♠Q, East has to throw one of his guards and the slam is yours. If you fail to duck the first trick, you will have to guess how the cards lie in the end position, rather than being able to claim.

63. MRS. HERON-WATSON'S ADVICE

In the first round of the Hampshire Knock-out Cup, the St. Titus team had been drawn against four churchwomen from the parish of Branston Heath. The match was to be played in their vicarage.

'Welcome, welcome, Abbot,' said Mrs. Heron-Watson, the vicar's wife. 'I can't say how much we've all been looking forward to this encounter.'

The Abbot summoned a cheery smile. 'Yes, we were pleased when we heard the draw, too,' he replied.

'It's so nice to have eight players of the same... well, the same persuasion,' continued Mrs. Heron-Watson. 'Perhaps it would be in order for you to say a small grace before we start, Abbot?'

No escape route suggested itself. Aware that Brother Paulo was finding it hard to keep a straight face, the Abbot muttered a few words. 'May the Lord make us truly thankful for the hands we receive tonight and er... may we all forgive any errors made by our team-mates.'

Mrs. Heron-Watson gave a little clap. 'Very nice, indeed, Abbot!' she exclaimed. 'Now, shall we start?'

The first half had not been long under way when Mrs. Heron-Watson arrived in a slam.

```
                    ♠ K J 3
                    ♡ Q J 8 6
                    ◇ A 8
                    ♣ A Q J 2
  ♠ 9 8 7 4      ┌─────────┐      ♠ 1 0 6 2
  ♡ 1 0 9 5 2    │Both Vul.│      ♡ K 7 3
  ◇ 1 0 5 4 3    │Dealer S │      ◇ K J 6
  ♣ 5            └─────────┘      ♣ 1 0 9 7 4
                    ♠ A Q 5
                    ♡ A 4
                    ◇ Q 9 7 2
                    ♣ K 8 6 3
```

West	North	East	South
Brother	Edith	The	Emmeline
Xavier	Blandish	Abbot	Heron-Watson
			1NT
pass	6NT	all pass	

Brother Xavier led the ♠8 and dummy's jack won the first trick. 'Queen of hearts, please,' said Mrs. Heron-Watson.

The Abbot followed with the ♡3 and the queen was run successfully. Declarer now cashed four rounds of clubs, followed by the ♡A and the two remaining spades. The lead was in dummy and these cards were still out:

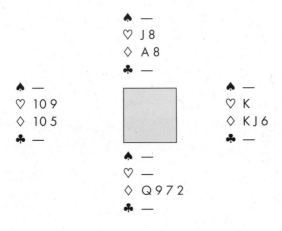

Mrs. Heron-Watson nodded her head thoughtfully. Perhaps leading the ♡8 now would be a good idea? If the Abbot's ♡K was bare, this would set up the ♡J for an extra trick. That would be clever! 'Eight of hearts, please, Edith,' she said.

The Abbot won with the ♡K and returned the ◇6. After considering the matter for a few seconds, Mrs. Heron-Watson saw no reason not to try her luck with the ◇Q. It won the trick, to her great excitement, and two further red-suit winners in the dummy gave her the slam.

'You made it?' exclaimed the white-haired Mrs. Blandish. 'Oh, well done, Emmeline. That was quite a tricky end position.'

Mrs. Heron-Watson appeared somewhat flushed by her success. 'It was a lucky lie of the cards, really,' she replied. 'The hand more or less played itself.'

Brother Xavier leaned forward. 'Isn't it better if you cover the queen of hearts, Abbot?' he suggested.

The Abbot, suddenly feeling very tired, returned his cards to the wallet. It seemed that Xavier was right. Should he have worked it out, somehow?

Mrs. Heron-Watson gave the Abbot a consoling pat on the hand. 'When I first started playing the game, my dear mother taught me a little rhyme,' she said.

> *Declarer will often score another,*
> *If his honor you don't cover.*

'I've found that most helpful over the years,' she continued. 'It's easier to remember something when it rhymes, don't you think?'

Master Point Press on the Internet

www.masterpointpress.com

Our main site, with information about our books and software, reviews and more.

www.masteringbridge.com

Our site for bridge teachers and students — free downloadable support material for our books, helpful articles, forums and more.

www.bridgeblogging.com

Read and comment on regular articles from MPP authors and other bridge notables.

www.ebooksbridge.com

Purchase downloadable electronic versions of MPP books.